ANALYTICAL METHODS DEVELOPED FOR APPLICATION TO LUNAR SAMPLES ANALYSES

A symposium
presented at the
Seventy-fifth Annual Meeting
AMERICAN SOCIETY FOR
TESTING AND MATERIALS
Los Angeles, Calif., 25–30 June 1972

ASTM SPECIAL TECHNICAL PUBLICATION 539
D. A. Flory, symposium chairman

List price $15.00
04-539000-38

 AMERICAN SOCIETY FOR TESTING AND MATERIALS
1916 Race Street, Philadelphia, Pa. 19103

© *by American Society for Testing and Materials* 1973
Library of Congress Catalog Card Number: 73-80189

NOTE

Printed in Baltimore, Md.
August 1973

Foreword

The symposium on Analytical Methods Developed for Application to Lunar Samples Analyses was given at the Seventy-fifth Annual Meeting of the American Society for Testing and Materials held in Los Angeles, Calif., 25-30 June 1972. Committee F-7 on Aerospace Industry Methods sponsored the symposium. D. A. Flory, University of Houston, presided as symposium chairman.

Related
ASTM Publications

Sampling of Soil and Rock, STP 483 (1971),
    $8.00 (04-483000-38)

Special Procedures for Testing Soil and Rock for
    Engineering Purposes, STP 479 (1970), $15.75
    (04-479000-38)

Contents

Introduction   1

Environmental Control of Lunar Samples in the Lunar Receiving
     Laboratory—*M. A. Reynolds, N. L. Turner, J. C. Hurgeton,*
       M. F. Barbee, D. A. Flory, and *B. R. Simoneit*   3
    Procedure of Contamination Control   7
    Results   10
    Conclusion   15

Organic Contamination Monitoring and Control in the Lunar Receiving
     Laboratory—*B. R. Simoneit, D. A. Flory,* and *M. A. Reynolds*   16
    Procedure for Contamination Control   18
    Experimental Procedures   20
    Discussion of Results   21
    Conclusions   33

Monitoring Systems for Evaluation of Terrestrial Contamination in a
     Lunar Sample Transfer Facility—*P. C. Wszolek, P. T. Holland,*
       W. H. McFadden, A. L. Burlingame, J. T. Wilder, and *B. R. Simoneit*   35
    Experimental Procedures   37
    Results and Applications   46
    Conclusions   54

Mass Spectrometric Analysis of the Volatiles Released by Heating or
     Crushing Rocks—*Colin Barker* and *M. A. Sommer*   56
    Apparatus   57
    Analytical Procedure   62
    Data Handling   64
    Results and Discussion   66
    Conclusions   69

Techniques for the Analysis of Gases Sequentially Released from Lunar
     Samples—*D. J. DesMarais, J. M. Hayes,* and *W. G. Meinschein*   71
    Equipment   72
    Sample Handling and Analytical Procedures   76

Microsampling Techniques for Infrared Spectroscopic Analysis of Lunar and Terrestrial Minerals–*P. A. Estep, J. J. Kovach,* and *C. Karr*   80
    Lunar Sample Studies   81
    Application of Microsampling Techniques in Terrestrial Mineral Analysis   88

Polarized Crystal-Field Spectra of Micro Particles of the Moon– *H. K. Mao* and *P. M. Bell*   100
    Instrumentation   101
    Lunar Crystals and Glass   104
    Spectra   106
    Spectra Measured at High Pressure   114
    Oxygen Fugacity of Lunar Lavas   117

Method for Ultra-Accurate Oxygen Determination for Rare Reference Samples–*A. Volborth, R. Dayal, P. McGhee,* and *S. Parikh*   120
    Equipment   121
    Specimens   121
    Experimental Procedure   124
    Discussion and Conclusions   126

Application of 14 MeV and Cf-252 Neutron Sources to Instrumental Neutron Activation Analysis of Lunar Samples–*Morteza Janghorbani, D. E. Gillum,* and *W. D. Ehmann*   128
    Nuclear Reactions   130
    Instrumentation and Techniques   130
    Results and Discussion   137
    Conclusion   138

Isotopic Abundance Determination of Submicro Amounts of Rhenium by Neutron Activation–*R. Michel, U. Herpers, H. Kulus,* and *W. Herr*   140
    Experimental   141
    Discussion   147

Introduction

This symposium was organized to provide an opportunity for those outside of the National Aeronautics and Space Administration lunar sample program to learn of some of the advances in methods and instrumentation resulting directly from the program. The papers included in these proceedings include two additional papers as well as eight papers presented at the symposium. The two papers were added in an attempt to broaden the coverage of the proceedings to include a more representative sampling of the many analytical techniques developed for lunar sample analysis. These proceedings still do not deal with all disciplines represented in the lunar sample program, but the methods covered appear to offer the greatest potential application to the analysis problems of many ASTM chemists.

The papers describe the present status of advanced testing methods used in lunar sample analysis. Particular emphasis is placed on the description and evaluation of the various experimental techniques as opposed to other lunar science conferences which have emphasized interpretation of the results. Since contamination control is such a vital consideration in lunar sample work, several papers are presented dealing with that aspect. Particulate and organic contamination control procedures and monitoring techniques developed for the Lunar Receiving Laboratory sample processing cabinets and individual principal investigators' installations are described. These techniques should have applications to problems of contamination control in the electronics manufacturing industry, the assembly of equipment for use in space, and many other situations where ultraclean particulate and organic contamination levels are required. Two of the papers deal with the analysis of trace volatiles in rocks released by heating and would seem to be candidate methods for the analysis of dissolved gases in metals and alloys. A microsampling technique for infrared vibrational spectroscopic analysis is described which allows one to obtain molecular structure information on isolated single 1200-150 μm mineral grains and on grains *in situ* in polished rocks. This technique should have application in material testing when only very small samples are available or for *in situ* studies of impurities or contaminants which degrade the properties of the parent material. Another technique utilizes polarized crystal-field spectra to obtain information on oxidation states of the trace elements iron, titanium, and chromium in silicate rocks. A similar technique may be useful in the study of ceramics or other related materials. One study examines the luminescence properties of lunar

1

samples to establish the extent to which rocks and minerals can be identified by luminescent spectra. Other methods of analysis described include scanning electron microscopy and neutron activation analysis. The potential application of these techniques to analytical problems in materials testing is certainly considerable, and many more possibilities beyond those briefly mentioned here will be recognized by those reading these proceedings.

D. A. Flory
Research Associate,
Department of Biophysical
Sciences, University of Houston,
Houston, Tex. 77004; symposium
chairman.

M. A. Reynolds,[1] *N. L. Turner,*[1] *J. C. Hurgeton,*[1] *M. F. Barbee,*[1]
D. A. Flory,[2] *and B. R. Simoneit* [3]

Environmental Control of Lunar Samples in the Lunar Receiving Laboratory

REFERENCE: Reynolds, M. A., Turner, N. L., Hurgeton, J. C., Barbee, M. F., Flory, D. A., and Simoneit, B. R., **"Environmental Control of Lunar Samples in the Lunar Receiving Laboratory,"** *Analytical Methods Developed for Application to Lunar Samples Analyses, ASTM STP 539,* American Society for Testing and Materials, 1973, pp. 3–15.

ABSTRACT: The arrival on Earth of samples of lunar rocks presented an unparalleled opportunity to expand man's knowledge of the solar system. Close control of the environment was necessary to maintain the integrity of the lunar material. This started with the development of high vacuum (10^{-6} to 10^{-8} torr) processing lines which were constructed of materials that would not interfere with the analyses of the lunar samples, and later (Apollo 14) evolved to the use of high-purity nitrogen filled cabinets or glove boxes when the vacuum lines were abandoned. Trace quantities of oxygen, argon, carbon dioxide, carbon monoxide, hydrogen, methane, and water in the nitrogen processing lines were analyzed. During Apollo 14, analysis at 1 in. negative pressure within cabinets, O_2 varied between 25 to 50 ppm, and moisture from 85 to 125 ppm. Following the elimination of quarantine restrictions, Apollo 15 samples were processed at a slight positive pressure which further reduced oxygen to 10 to 30 ppm and moisture to 15 to 25 ppm. Equipment and cabinetry interiors were cleaned consistently to low levels of hydrocarbons and particulate contaminants. The maximum allowable hydrocarbons, C_{10} through C_{30} was 10 micrograms per square foot of critical surface and flush samples with particles over 750 μm in size required recleaning. This resulted in providing the scientific community with samples whose integrity had not been compromised during preliminary investigations and allocations.

KEY WORDS: lunar geology, lunar rocks, lunar dust, lunar analysis, moisture meters, gas analysis, gas chromatography, terrestrial contamination, inventory control, glove boxes, contamination, cleaning, particles

[1] Contamination control officer, research analyst, quality engineer, and particle control specialist, respectively, National Aeronautics and Space Administration-Manned Spacecraft Center, Houston, Tex., 77058.

[2] Research associate, Department of Biophysical Sciences and Chemistry, University of Houston, Houston, Tex. 77004.

[3] Specialist, Space Sciences Laboratory, University of California, Berkeley, Calif. 94720.

3

The arrival on Earth of lunar rocks and lunar soil samples presents an unparalleled opportunity to expand man's knowledge of the solar system. For the first time it has been possible to examine thoroughly and minutely extraterrestrial material which has not been exposed to the earth's environment. The pristine integrity of the lunar samples could only be realized by carefully controlling the types of material, procedures in processing, cleanliness of all materials, and control of the gases used to blanket the samples.

The purpose of this paper is to describe the contamination controls used in the Lunar Receiving Laboratory (LRL) during processing of lunar samples, and to summarize the particulate and trace gas results obtained so far.

The first step in contamination control was to make sure that the Apollo lunar sample return containers (ALSRC) did not contribute significant amounts of contamination[1].[4] Therefore, materials of construction, cleaning techniques, and handling procedures were developed and rigidly controlled. These constraints were then imposed on all lunar tools, containers, and sample facilities used in the program.

When the lunar samples returned to Earth, facilities were required to investigate and process the samples while maintaining their integrity. The LRL was established as the primary facility for initially examining the samples. The LRL has four major functions[2]. These are:

1. Quarantining and testing of the lunar samples, spacecraft, and astronauts, for potentially harmful contamination of extraterrestrial origin.

2. Permanent storage under vacuum of a portion of the samples from each mission.

3. Performance of scientific investigations of samples that were time-critical.

4. Distribution of lunar samples to the scientific community for detailed investigations.

The LRL, Fig. 1, includes two distinct areas within the same building. One area is a normal laboratory, whereas the second area is behind a biological barrier that completely isolated the lunar samples, the returned spacecraft, and the astronauts for the 21-day quarantine period[2].

Within this biological barrier area are the facilities used to perform time-critical scientific investigations such as radiation counting, those facilities used in sample distribution, and the facilities used for quarantine testing. The latter consists of a cabinet barrier system or glove boxes within which the tests on the lunar samples are conducted in further isolation from the rest of the laboratory.

Initially, the lunar sample containers were opened, and the material was examined in a vacuum complex (10^{-6} to 10^{-8} torr) with appproximated lunar surface conditions, while at the same time minimizing terrestrial contamination.

[4] The italic numbers in brackets refer to the list of references appended to this paper.

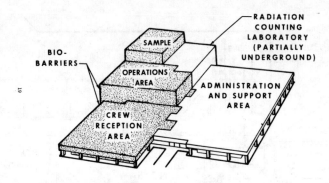

FIG. 1–*Lunar receiving laboratory, function areas.*

The process of examining and distributing the samples from this vacuum complex was time consuming and operations were awkward. During both Apollo 11 and 12 missions portions of the lunar samples were processed for allocation in a small sterile glove box in a dry nitrogen atmosphere. Since this proved to be a much easier and quicker method of processing and did not degrade the integrity of the samples, the scientific community, which has guided all of the LRL activities through a series of committees, agreed after Apollo 12 that processing in the vacuum complex was not necessary. A new system was installed based upon the experience gained from the small glove box. This system uses dry nitrogen as an environmental blanket and has the capability of being sterilized and of maintaining this sterility. This line is appropriately called the sterile nitrogen atmosphere processing (SNAP) line, Fig. 2, and was used for Apollo 14, 15, and 16 lunar sample processing.

The orderly and speedy processing of the lunar samples gave recurrent problems, mainly because the quantity of sample material increased with each succeeding mission. After the second mission, Apollo 12, a decision was made to build an additional processing line. In this line lunar samples which had been exposed to earth's atmosphere, for example, rocks brought back in unsealable bags, were processed. Even though the lunar samples had some history of atmospheric contamination, this type of processing would prevent further contamination, for example, rusting. This line also used nitrogen as an environmental blanket, but the cabinet sterility could not be maintained, and so was appropriately named the nonsterile nitrogen processing line (NNPL), Fig. 3. This line was also used for Apollo 14, 15, and 16 lunar sample processing.

To maintain the integrity of the lunar samples during the LRL processing, the materials which came in contact with the samples were controlled rigidly. Materials of construction of the cabinetry, tools, and equipment were limited to

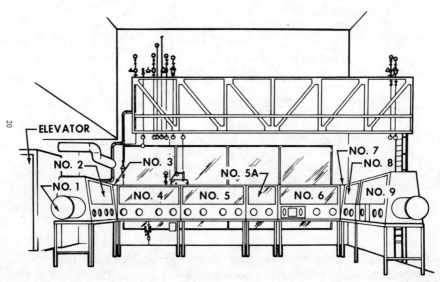

20

FIG. 2–*Sterile nitrogen atmosphere processing line.*

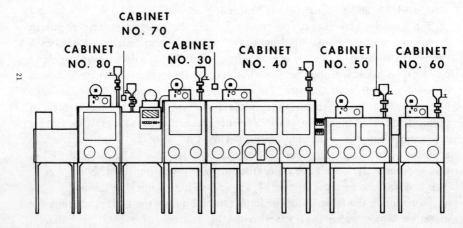

21

FIG. 3–*Nonsterile nitrogen processing line.*

stainless steel, aluminum, teflon, rubber gloves, viton, and glass. These materials were selected because they were easily identifiable in most methods of lunar sample analysis. In addition, test coupons representative of the base material making up the cabinets, equipment, or tools or all three have been placed on file for future analysis should a question ever arise as to the exact composition.

One of the obvious possibilities for sample contamination is from the nitrogen used to blanket the SNAP and NNPL lines. Liquid nitrogen (LN_2) is purchased to the specifications shown in Table 1. The LN_2 is vaporized and this gaseous nitrogen (GN_2) is used to blanket the processing cabinetry. One of the problems encountered with the LN_2 supplied by cryogenic manufacturing companies in the Houston area was a high argon content, 800 to 1200 ppm. To remedy the situation, an LN_2 plant in Mississippi where the argon was in the 10 to 20 ppm range was substituted.

The guiding philosophy of contamination control in the LRL has been to eliminate all environmental contaminants possible but, where contamination cannot be eliminated, to limit these contaminants to a few easily identifiable materials at the lowest levels practical.

The types of contamination of major concern may be grouped as follows:

(*a*) Those contaminants which would alter or change the samples. Moisture and oxygen are examples of this type of contamination. These have to be controlled very carefully and monitored accurately.

(*b*) Contaminants which would interfere with the analysis of the samples. Organic and particulate contamination are examples of this group.

Procedures of Contamination Control

Contamination control procedures in the LRL consisted of trace gas and moisture, processing line cleanliness, particulate contamination, and organic contamination.

Trace Gas and Moisture

Trace gas analysis of oxygen, argon, carbon dioxide, carbon monoxide, hydrogen, methane, and water was conducted during mission operations. A

TABLE 1—*Maximum allowable limits of tract gas contaminants.*

Contaminant	ppm
Argon	20
Oxygen	10
Carbon monoxide	10
Carbon dioxide	10
Hydrogen	10
Moisture	10
Methane	1

Varian-Aerograph Model 1732-20 trace gas analyzer was used to monitor the volatile gases in the nitrogen glove boxes. The moisture was analyzed using a Panametrics Model 1000 hygrometer. A Teledyne trace oxygen analyzer Model 316-1 was also used to monitor oxygen.

Processing Line Cleanliness

The tools and equipment used to process the lunar samples were cleaned to requirements established by the LRL[3]. A main facility was designed to clean the bulk of the tools and equipment at the White Sands Test Facility. Contingency cleaning facilities for items requiring quick turn-around times were also developed within the LRL.

There was, however, no previous history on cleaning anything the size or shape of the SNAP and NNPL cabinets to the desired low levels of hydrocarbon (THC) and particulate. Therefore, one cabinet of the SNAP line was used to develop the techniques experimentally and set the cleanliness levels for the balance of the SNAP and NNPL lines, and, incidently, in the curator's laboratory facilities as well. The procedure was as follows: The technician wearing clean room clothing entered the cabinet and completely washed all areas inside the cabinet using a 1 percent soap solution, Fig. 4. In addition, he scrubbed and polished the cabinet surfaces. He then examined all interior surfaces with a black light. If there was fluorescence, he recleaned the fluorescent areas until there was no change in fluorescence. The technician then exited the cabinet and subsequent cleaning was accomplished through the glove ports.

The soap solution was removed with repeated distilled or deionized water rinses and subsequent removal of the rinse water. The flush fluids were contained in 5-gal stainless steel pressure vessels and pressurized with pure N_2 gas to approximately 85 psig for maximum effectiveness in removing particulate.

Immediately after removal of the water, the entire interior of the cabinet was rinsed with isopropyl alcohol (nanograde) (IPA) sprayed through the glove ports. In-line filters were used at the spray head to ensure particulate free flush fluids. After removal of the IPA, all areas were rinsed with a minimum of 500 ml of redistilled Freon 113 (trichlorotrifluoroethane) per square foot of cabinet surface (most cabinets contain about 50 square feet of surface). A final flush using redistilled Freon 113 was sprayed over the entire cabinet interior for final verification of cabinet cleanliness, both for particulate count and THC. A positive GN_2 purge was then maintained on the clean cabinet.

Particulate Contamination

Particulate testing was conducted in the SNAP and NNPL lines after the cabinetry was cleaned but prior to the introduction of tools and equipment. This was done to obtain an estimate of cabinet cleanliness before each mission. The particle testing consisted of placing fallout coupons in various sections of the

FIG. 4–*NASA S-71-56921. First step in cleaning processing lines.*

cabinets for extended periods of time, 4 to 6 days. The cabinets were in the quiescent state during testing. The fallout strips were then counted and analyzed.

Organic Contamination

An elaborate program to control the types and amounts of organic contamination was initiated prior to the first lunar landing, Apollo 11, and is continuing[4,5]. This part of contamination control will be discussed in another paper presented at this symposium.[5]

[5] See p. 16.

Results

Trace Gas and Moisture Control

With the establishment of SNAP and NNPL as the major lunar sample processing lines for Apollo 14 and subsequent missions, it was decided that certain gas contaminants should be maintained at a minimum level. Trace gas analysis of oxygen, argon, carbon dioxide, carbon monoxide, hydrogen, methane, and water was carried out during mission operations. The data collected during the missions from the processing lines are similar; therefore, only the SNAP line will be discussed in this paper. During Apollo 14 the lunar sample processing lines were sterilized with ethylene oxide and run at negative 1-in. water gage pressure (relative to the room) due to quarantine requirements. In Fig. 5 the daily high-oxygen and moisture values are plotted. The oxygen could be maintained between 10 and 15 ppm and the moisture between 15 and 20 ppm in the static mode. However, during operations the values increased for oxygen to 25 to 30 ppm and moisture to 85 to 125 ppm.

The high values in Fig. 5 can be explained as glove failures, opening of sterilized equipment which was bagged, and by peracetic acid sterilization cycle of inbound equipment followed by a distilled water flush.

The argon values varied from 10 to 30 ppm the majority of the time with the highest value being 300 ppm which correlated with a very high-oxygen value. Examination of a plot of argon showed the same trends as oxygen, which would be expected for air contamination. Of the other measured contaminants, only carbon dioxide gave values above the detection limits of 1 ppm, but it never rose above 10 ppm.

Apollo 15 was the first mission in which there was no quarantine requirement for the crew or the lunar samples, and, as a result, the processing lines were not sterilized. This significantly reduced the amount of certain contaminants and afforded the opportunity to improve on cabinet cleanliness. In addition, the lines were operated at a positive 1-in. water gage pressure (relative to the room) which decreased the amount of atmospheric contamination. In Fig. 6 the daily high oxygen and moisture values for those cabinets in which lunar samples were exposed are plotted. The oxygen and moisture levels in the static mode were less than 10 ppm in all cabinets. During the processing the oxygen varied from 10 to 30 ppm and moisture from 15 to 25 ppm. In the beginning of the processing of the samples the values were higher, but, as the activities decreased, the daily high values decreased. The abnormally high values of oxygen and water were due to operations involving the vacuum dusting of lunar rocks. The vacuum system capacity exceeded the gaseous nitrogen flow to the cabinet and readmitted gases from the exhaust header. The exhaust gases were high in oxygen and water due to transfers into the processing line. This was corrected by increasing the normal flow of nitrogen to the cabinet during vacuum dusting operations.

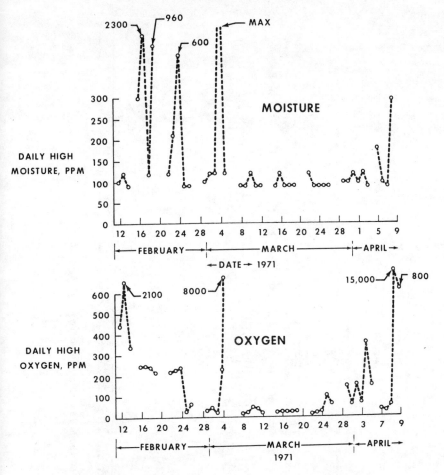

FIG. 5—*Apollo 15 moisture and oxygen daily high values.*

On 9 Sept. 1971, a hurricane alert for this area was put in effect. The processing lines were secured by placing them under static pressure to safeguard the lines in case of loss of nitrogen or electrical power. During this static phase of operation, the moisture level rose to approximately 200 ppm.

The values for carbon dioxide, carbon monoxide, methane, and hydrogen were always below the detection limit of 1 ppm. The argon value varied between 5 and 30 ppm.

Processing Line Cleanliness

The tools and equipment used to process the lunar samples were cleaned to a very low level of organic contamination, less than 1 ng (10^{-9}) of total

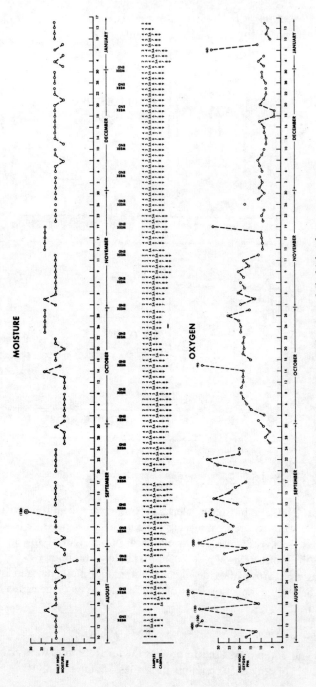

FIG. 6—*Apollo 15 moisture and oxygen daily high values.*

hydrocarbon contamination (THC), in the C_{10} to C_{30} range per square centimeter of exposed surface[3]. The particulate contamination level for these tools and equipment was set at the cleanest level which had been achievable during the Apollo Project. Thus, the organic and particulate levels of the tools and processing equipment were controlled very carefully at levels which would ensure minimum interference with subsequent analyses.

These cleanliness levels were maintained both at the White Sands Test Facility and in the LRL contingency cleaning rooms.

After repeated attempts at cleaning the experimental cabinet the cleanliness level of Table 2 was established and adhered to for all subsequent cabinet cleaning.

Particles

On Apollo 14 the majority of the particulate contamination as determined by microprobe analysis was silicon, metallics, and Teflon. The metallics and Teflon were due mainly to shredding of the aluminum foil and Teflon.

Because organic monitors were not used on Apollo 15 the microprobe analyses of fallout particulate indicated only metallics and Teflon.

One of the problems associated with attempting to control the particulate environment of the lunar samples is the inability to completely clean particles from a surface. Figure 7 shows a foreign particle embedded in aluminum foil which had been previously cleaned to a level where a flush sample obtained from the aluminum surface yielded no particles greater than 5 μm in size. Additional particulate problems were encountered with shedding of aluminum foil and Teflon bags.

A particularly troublesome recurrent problem has been static generation associated with Teflon bags and sheets. This causes any particles in the vicinity

TABLE 2—*Processing line cleanliness level.*

		THC
Particle count:[a]		
0 to 175 μm	unlimited[b]	10 μg/ft^2
175 to 700 μm	6	
700 μm	zero	(base sample must
Fibers:[c]		have less than 2
700 to 1500 μm	1	μg/100-ml sample)
1500 μm	zero	

[a] Total number of particles in 100-ml sample.

[b] Unlimited means that particles in this range are not counted; however, any obscuring of the filter grid lines shall be cause for rejection.

[c] Fibers—a particle whose length is 10 times its width (minimum length of 100).

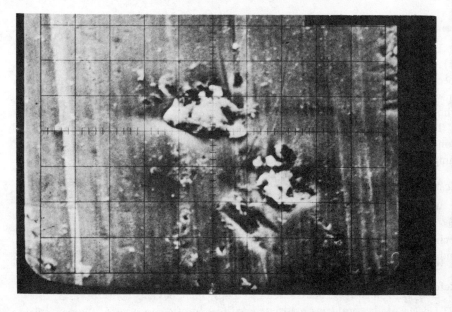

FIG. 7–*SL 0073(2)-Foreign particle embedded in aluminum foil* × 250.

of the Teflon to be attracted to it and is particularly noticeable with fibers from clean room clothing and gloves. Extensive use has been made of black light (ultraviolet) to detect these fibers and then either flushing with Freon, vacuuming, or blowing them off with pure N_2.

The data in Table 3 indicate that a decided improvement has been made in the control of the cabinet particulate contamination for Apollo 16 over 15; and Apollo 15 was likewise much better than Apollo 14.

TABLE 3–*Summary of fallout particle counts, Apollo 15 and 16.*

	Particle Range and Number[a]				
	10 to 25 μm	25 to 50 μm	50 to 100 μm	100 to 175 μm	>175
Apollo 15 mission	96.0	32.5	8.0	1.5	1.5
Apollo 16 mission	25.0	5.0	2.3	0.2	0.2

[a] Averages of several readings (N = 6 for 15 and N = 24 for Apollo 16).

Conclusion

The goal of the environmental control program established at the LRL was: 1) to provide the scientific community with samples processed to their specifications and free of trace amounts of terrestrial contamination and (2) to provide future scientists with the opportunity to experiment on lunar samples whose integrity has been maintained.

The success of this program was witnessed in the Third Annual Lunar Science Conference held in Houston, January 1972, where scientists reported on lunar samples that were nearly free of contamination by terrestrial materials[6].

Acknowledgments

We thank W. Hirsh and the Gas Analysis Laboratory for performing the trace gas analysis work, K. Suit and his Laboratory Operations Branch for their technical assistance, L. Caldwell and his technicians for performing the cleaning, and L. Schluter for performing much of the particulate contamination analyses.

References

1] Liddle, R. H. et al, *Heating Piping and Air Conditioning,* Vol. 42, No. 11, Nov. 1970.
2] McClane, J. C. Jr., et al, *Science,* Vol. 155, 1967, pp. 525-529.
3] Lunar Receiving Laboratory Cleaning Procedures for Contamination Control, MSCM-03243, National Aeronautics and Space Administration-Manned Spacecraft Center, Houston, Tex., 1972.
4] Simoneit, B. R. and Flory, D. A., "Apollo 11, 12 and 13 Organic Contamination Monitoring History," National Aeronautics and Space Administration-Manned Spacecraft Center, Special Report, in press.
5] Flory, D. A. and Simoneit, B. R., "Terrestrial Contamination in Apollo Lunar Samples," *Space Life Sciences,* in press.
6] King, E. A., Heymann, D. J., and Criswell, D. R., eds., *Proceedings,* Third Lunar Science Conference, *Geochimica et Cosmochimica Acta,* Supplement 3, The MIT Press, Cambridge, Mass., 1972.

B. R. Simoneit,[1] D. A. Flory,[2] and M. A. Reynolds[3]

Organic Contamination Monitoring and Control in the Lunar Receiving Laboratory

REFERENCE: Simoneit, B. R., Flory, D. A., and Reynolds, M. A., "Organic Contamination Monitoring and Control in the Lunar Receiving Laboratory," *Analytical Methods Developed for Application to Lunar Samples Analyses, ASTM STP 539,* American Society for Testing and Materials, 1973, pp. 16–34.

ABSTRACT: The assessment of the indigenous organic matter in returned lunar samples has been a primary scientific goal of the Apollo program. The levels of such indigenous organic material were expected to be and found to be small. The pristine integrity of the lunar samples, however, could only be realized by carefully controlling the collection, processing, and analyzing of lunar samples so they might remain free of any significant levels (average laboratory detection limit of 10^{-9} g/g) of terrestrial contamination.

The primary purpose of this paper is to describe the contamination control procedures adopted to meet these requirements, to present briefly the analytical evidence obtained throughout the program on potential contamination sources, and to summarize the types and levels of organic contaminants actually found in the lunar samples.

The control of potential organic contamination of the lunar samples has consisted of: (*a*) severe limitations on materials which "see" or contact the lunar samples, (*b*) isolation of the sample in controlled environments at all times, (*c*) development of procedures to clean all surfaces which come into direct contact or may "see" the samples, and (*d*) strict controls on fabrication, processing, and handling of all lunar sample hardware. Materials actually contacting the lunar sample have been limited to stainless steel, aluminum alloy, and Teflon. Samples were handled under clean vacuum or nitrogen environments whenever possible. Cleaning methods capable of achieving total organic contamination levels on surfaces of less than 10^{-9} g/cm^2 were implemented for all surfaces contacting lunar samples.

A contamination monitoring scheme was put into effect to assist in the evaluation of cleaning procedures and to assess the quantity and type of organic contamination that finds its way into the samples despite the controls discussed. This consisted of the analysis of: (1) York mesh samples or

[1] Specialist, Space Sciences Laboratory, University of California, Berkeley, Calif. 94720.

[2] Research associate, Department of Biophysical Sciences, University of Houston, Houston, Tex. 77004.

[3] Contamination control officer, National Aeronautics and Space Administration-Manned Spacecraft Center, Houston, Tex. 77058.

aluminum foil processed with the flight Apollo lunar sample return containers (ALSRC); (2) the analysis of solvent wash samples used to clean all Lunar Receiving Laboratory (LRL) sample processing tools, cabinets, equipment, and containers; (3) the analysis of lunar module (LM) exhaust gas products; and (4) the analysis of sintered samples of Ottawa sand exposed to the various processing cabinets in the LRL.

Monitoring of the processing activities in the Lunar Receiving Laboratory during simulations prior to Apollo 11 indicated that organic contamination levels as high as 1000 ppm might be introduced to the lunar samples. Procedural and handling improvements reduced this level to less than 1 ppm during processing of Apollo 11 lunar material. Further controls, more thorough cleaning and greater attention to potential sources of contamination reduced the level to less than 0.1 ppm during Apollo 12 sample processing. Preliminary data indicate the levels for the Apollo 14 and 15 sample processing were also less than 0.1 ppm. The major contaminants found in the lunar samples (mainly, Apollo 11 and 12) consisted mainly of hydrocarbons, phthalate esters, LM exhaust products, plastics—Teflon, Mylar, etc., and some silicones.

It can be concluded that a contamination control plan has been successfully developed and implemented, providing investigators with lunar samples containing less than 0.1-ppm total organic contamination, which is as low or lower than the experimental blanks obtained in organic geochemical research laboratories.

KEY WORDS: lunar analysis, organic matter, lunar geology, contamination, cleaning monitors, organic chemistry, mass spectrometry

The return of lunar samples by the Apollo missions was seen to offer a unique opportunity to study extraterrestrial material free from the ambiguous findings of meteorite analyses. Such an opportunity would not present itself again for a long time to come. In the past, meteorite analyses have not accounted for terrestrial organic contamination acquired during the fall, recovery, and storage. The analysis of pristine lunar material was anticipated to yield information on the extraterrestrial occurrence of carbonaceous matter, leading to a further understanding of the basic hypotheses of chemical evolution and the origin of life. Thus, an assessment of the nature and amount of organic matter present in returned lunar material has been one of the major scientific goals of the Apollo programs.

From the beginning of Apollo science planning, organic geo- and cosmochemists have realized that only small amounts of organic matter would be likely found indigenous to the lunar material. Such low concentrations of organic matter however, can be easily detected by the analytical instrumentation used in organic geochemistry (usual detection limit 1×10^{-9} g). The combination of these two facts made it clear that the integrity of the lunar samples could be only maintained by carefully controlling the collection, processing, and analyses of the lunar material and thus keeping the contamination levels to a minimum. It was also stressed that the number of different contaminants should be minimized, since the presence of a few compounds in known and reproducible quantities is a situation much easier to deal with than a wide spectrum of compounds whose total concentration is of equal magnitude. Maintaining this type and level of contamination control would then allow definitive conclusions to be drawn concerning the true source of organic compounds present in less than part per million quantities. Such low levels of indigenous organic matter, indeed, have been confirmed for the lunar samples returned through the Apollo 15 mission [1-10].[4]

Procedures for Contamination Control

To achieve the goals just outlined it was necessary to: (a) identify potential sources of terrestrial contamination; (b) measure the actual amounts reaching the lunar sample from these various potential sources (are they sufficient to invalidate or seriously degrade organic geochemical investigations); and (c) specify the necessary requirements and protocol to assure that such contamination would be held within the specified amounts.

The various potential sources of organic contamination which exist throughout the entire lunar sample collection and analysis procedure beginning with the Apollo lunar sample return container (ALSRC) in which the samples are stored during return to earth, continuing through processing and distribution of these samples in the Lunar Receiving Laboratory (LRL), and finally the actual laboratory analyses are given next and the relevant items will be discussed further.

1. Surface contamination of the ALSRC and its outbound contents.

2. Surface contamination on the Apollo lunar hand tools at the time they are used to obtain samples on the lunar surface.

3. Exhaust products deposited on the lunar surface by the lunar module (LM) descent engine and reaction control system (RCS) engines.

4. Outgassing of the LM and other lunar surface equipment deposited on the lunar surface.

5. Astronaut suit leakage deposited on lunar material prior to or during collection.

6. Particulate material abraded from the astronaut's suit or other lunar surface equipment during activities.

7. Venting of the LM fuel and oxidizer tanks, cabin, and waste system, and the portable life support system (PLSS) (back pack).

8. Contamination introduced by exposing the sample to the vacuum or alternately, nitrogen environments of the LRL sample processing lines.

9. Surface contamination on tools used to process lunar samples in the LRL processing lines, including the storage containers.

---

[4] The italic numbers in brackets refer to the list of references appended to this paper.

10. Surface contamination on containers used to distribute samples to principal investigators for analysis.

11. Artifacts from laboratory analysis procedures and instrumentation. Analyses of the various sources and considerations of their relative contaminant contributions led to the conclusions that items 4 through 6 were the least detrimental and for items 1 through 3 and 8 through 10 the types and quantities of organic contaminants could be assessed and controlled. Control of item 11 was left to the various individual investigators.

Generally the control of potential organic contamination of the lunar samples has been accomplished by severe limitations on materials which "see" or contact the lunar samples, isolation of the samples in controlled environments at all times, development of procedures to clean all surfaces which come into direct contact or may "see" the samples, and strict controls on fabrication, processing and handling of all lunar sample hardware. Materials actually contacting the lunar sample are limited to stainless steel, aluminum alloy, and Teflon (FEP). Materials which may "see" the lunar sample during collection, storage, and processing include the foregoing and Viton B, silicone rubber, Pyrex glass, indium-silver alloy, and molybdenum disulfide lubricant.

Cleaning methods [11] capable of achieving total organic contamination levels on surfaces of less than 10^{-9} g/cm^2 were developed. All surfaces coming into direct contact with lunar sample (ALSRC, lunar surface, LRL tools, and all sample containers) are required to be cleaned to this level. The cleaning procedure developed to produce these levels includes presoaking in PCA Freon; precleaning by ultrasonication first in detergent solution (1 percent Alconox), next three times in distilled water, and then in isopropyl alcohol; cleaning by ultrasonication in benzene-methanol solution (3:1, nanograde purity); and final rinsing by a pressurized spray using either PCA Freon or 3:1 benzene-methanol solution (both of nanograde purity). The cleaning steps are carried out in successively cleaner areas with the final rinse being conducted in a Class 100 clean room (Federal Standard 209a, 1966). Each cleaned item is then heat sealed into two successive Teflon bags (FEP Type A, also cleaned by the same procedure), each filled with nitrogen (filtered dry and sterile), which are then heat sealed into a nitrogen-filled clean polyethylene, polyvinyl chloride, or nylon bag. Similar cleaning techniques to obtain less stringent cleanliness levels were developed for the processing cabinets and other equipment which would "see" the samples but never come into direct contact with them.

The question of how the final state of cleanliness is determined was given considerable thought early in the program. Practical aspects related to the large volumes of cleaning which had to be carried out required that any cleanliness certification test used should be rapid and simple. The method actually used involves extracting the organic monitors (for example, Ottawa sand or York mesh—a woven aluminum alloy) or collecting aliquots of the final rinse solutions used in the cleaning procedures, vacuum evaporation of the solvent at room temperature, and determination of the amount of residue either by direct weighing or gas chromatography (GC) of an aliquot of the residue dissolved in a suitable solvent. The gas chromatograph response was correlated with the amount of residue by integrating the total area of all peaks eluted and multiplying them by a calibration factor and the appropriate dilution factor. Correlation of the area rinsed with the amounts of residue allows a calculation of the contamination per unit area. The disadvantages of the direct weighing method are lower sensitivity and inclusion of particulate inorganic material in the residue. The gas chromatographic method has the disadvantage of detecting only C_{12} to C_{30} hydrocarbons and other nonpolar compounds with similar retention times. It was found, however, that these types of compounds are the most common and ubiquitous contaminants, and demonstrating their absence results in stronger confidence that other organic material was not present. Many of the extract residues were analyzed by high resolution mass spectrometry to identify the volatilizable organic compounds present in the mixtures. This method is, however, not suitable for quantitative analysis.

Experimental Procedures

A contamination monitoring scheme was put into effect to assist in the evaluation of cleaning procedures and to obtain the maximum analytical information possible concerning the quantity and type of organic contamination which finds its way into the lunar samples despite the controls discussed. This scheme has involved the analyses of the following: York mesh samples or aluminum foil processed with the flight ALSRC's; solvent wash samples used to clean all LRL sample processing tools, cabinets, equipment, and containers; LM engine exhaust gas products; and sintered samples of Ottawa sand exposed to the various processing cabinets in the LRL. Analyses of the York mesh samples were accomplished by solvent extraction and subsequent GC analysis, low resolution mass spectrometry, and high resolution mass spectrometry of the extracted residues [12-14]. LRL hardware cleaning was evaluated by GC and high resolution mass spectrometric analyses of the solvent washing residues [12-15]. Analyses of the Ottawa sand monitors exposed during LRL processing were done by direct pyrolysis (500°C) mass spectrometry in the LRL [12], and additionally aliquots of the sand were provided to several investigators who received lunar samples.

The high resolution mass spectrometric analyses were carried out at dynamic resolutions of 8000 to 12,000, depending on the type of sample, using an AEI MS-902 mass spectrometer online to an XDS Sigma-7 computer [16-18]. The samples were introduced via a direct inlet probe into the ion source operated at the following conditions: ionizing current 500 μA, ionizing energy 70 eV, and temperature 200 to 220°C. The scan rate was 16 per decade at a data clock rate of 24 kHz. Low resolution mass spectra were determined using the same instrument. All GC analyses were carried out using either a Varian-Aerograph Model 204 GC or a Perkin-Elmer Model 900 GC with packed stainless steel columns.

A special processing cabinet system was set up at the University of California at Berkeley for processing the Apollo 14 and 15 prime organic samples returned in the special environment sample containers (SESC) [19-22]. A Varian-Aerograph Model 1732-20 trace gas analyzer was used to monitor volatile gases in the nitrogen or helium-filled cabinet system. A dichloromethane-filled bubbler was used to sample the cabinet atmosphere supply and exhaust, and alumina plaques and Ottawa sand were exposed to monitor the actual processing operations. This facility is discussed in detail in another paper presented at this symposium.[5]

The parallel particulate contamination monitoring and control program for the Apollo missions is discussed in another paper presented at this symposium.[6]

Discussion of Results

The LM and RCS engines are the least controllable sources of organic contamination listed in the previous section. An experimental program was carried out to trap the exhaust gases, and analyze and identify the organic combustion products. The results of that study have been detailed elsewhere [23,24], but the instrumental techniques applied to that study have been successfully used throughout the various monitoring programs. Virtually all LM engine exhaust products are low molecular weight, the bulk being free and combined gaseous products (mainly nitrogen, oxygen, carbon dioxide, water, carbon monoxide, and ammonia, with minor amounts of acetylene, hydrogen cyanide, formaldehyde, nitric oxide, cyanic acid, nitrogen dioxide, and formic acid). As such, they do not constitute a significant potential contamination source of the lunar surface due to their rapid diffusion over large areas. The solvent soluble organic products are quite varied in composition and very minor in concentration, accounting for only 12 percent of the exhaust products collected in the extraction solvents [23,24].

In order to illustrate the types of analytical data which were determined for the various monitors, two samples from the York mesh series were chosen as examples. The ALSRC's and various associated hardware were cleaned at Union Carbide Corporation, Nuclear Division, for all the Apollo missions. Each ALSRC cleaning was monitored by cleaning a set of three York mesh coils with the batch hardware. One coil was removed from each ALSRC and constituted the control sample. Two coils remained in each ALSRC during the LRL sterilization bakeout, and a second coil was removed just prior to sealing the ALSRC for

[5] See p. 35
[6] See p. 3

lunar transit. This constituted the F-250 sterilization monitor. The ALSRC
were each monitored from the LRL to the lunar surface with the remaining
York mesh coil. This flight organic monitor was sealed in its Teflon bag by the
astronauts as soon as the ALSRC was opened on the lunar surface. The solvent
soluble contamination levels of these York mesh coils from the various mission
are summarized in Table 1.

The data for the Apollo 14 lunar transit monitor from ALSRC 1006 are
shown in Figs. 1 and 2. The GC trace (Fig. 1a) represents approximately 1

TABLE 1–*The organic contamination levels of the ALSRC[a]*
York mesh coupon monitors.

ALSRC[a] No.	Description	Level (ng/cm^2)
Apollo 11:		
1004	control (cleaned at LRL)	895
1004	F-250[b] bake 160 C	710
1004	control (cleaned at LRL)	630
1004	F-250[b] bake 120 C	1160
1003 or 1004	lunar transit	lost at LRL
Apollo 12:		
1008	control (cleaned at UCC) duplicate	51 and 208
1008	F-250 bake 160 C	80
1009	control (cleaned at UCC)	50
1009	F-250 bake 160 C	80
1008	lunar transit	lost at LRL
1009	lunar transit	1210
Apollo 13:		
1002	control (cleaned at UCC)	not received for analysis
1002	F-250 bake 160 C	120
1005	control (cleaned at UCC)	not received for analysis
1005	F-250 bake 160 C	150
1002 and 1005	lunar transit	aborted
Apollo 14:		
1006 and 1007	controls (cleaned at UCC)	3.3 to 39.5 avg 17.7
1006	F-250 bake 160 C	155.0
1007	F-250 bake 160 C	56.3
1006	lunar transit	103.0
1007	lunar transit	49.6
Apollo 15:		
1011	control (cleaned at UCC)	86.0
1011	F-250 bake 160 C	55.0
1012	control (cleaned at UCC)	187.0
1012	F-250 bake 160 C	18.0
1013	control (cleaned at UCC)	108.0
1011	lunar transit	35.4
1012	lunar transit	17.6
Apollo 16:		
Not yet received for analysis		

[a] Apollo lunar sample return container.
[b] LRL cabinet number.

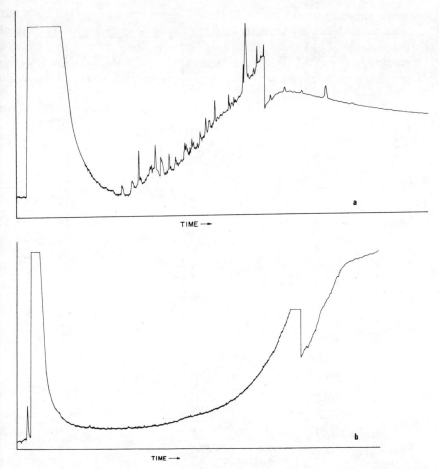

Conditions: 100 ft by 0.03 in. inside diameter stainless steel capillary column coated with OV-101, temperature hold at 45 C for 12 min, then programmed to 235 C at 2 C/min. Injector and manifold temperatures 220 and 300 C, respectively. Minimum detection level 5 ng/peak in the C_{10} to C_{30} hydrocarbon range.

FIG. 1–(a) *GC trace of the benzene and methanol extract residue (10 percent injection) of the Apollo 14 lunar transit monitor from ALSRC 1006. (b) GC trace of the residue (total injection) from an equivalent volume of benzene and methanol.*

percent of the total extract residue, whereas the blank GC trace (Fig. 1*b*) represents an equivalent amount of extraction solvent (3:1 benzene and methanol–200 ml). The largest peak in the GC trace has the relative retention time of dioctyl phthalate. The high resolution mass spectrometric data (Fig. 2) indicate mainly hydrocarbons of the series C_nH_{2n+2} to C_nH_{2n-20} for $n = 3$

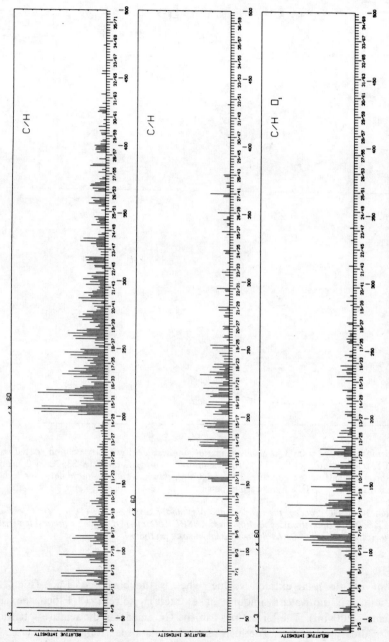

FIG. 2.–(a and b) High resolution mass spectrometric data for the benzene and methanol extract residue of the Apollo 14 lunar transit monitor from ALSRC 1006.

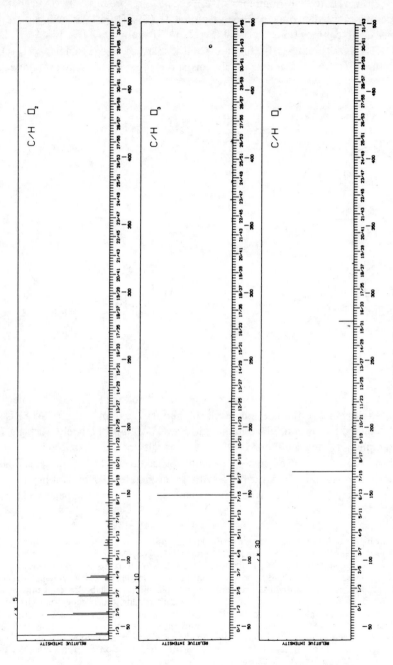

FIG. 2–*Continued.*

to 34; however, not all homologs of each series are present. The oxygenated compounds consist mainly of dioctyl phthalate (Structure I) as deduced from the peaks of compositions $C_8H_5O_3$ (Structure II–compare C/H_3 plot[7] of Fig. 2), $C_8H_7O_4$ (Structure III–compare C/HO_4 plot of Fig. 2) and $C_{16}H_{23}O_4$ (Structure IV). Minor amounts of phenols and carboxylic acids are also present.

Analyses of York mesh samples from the Apollo 11 mission (Table 1) indicated organic contamination levels of about 1 $\mu g/cm^2$ in the ALSRC's, which could have produced contamination levels of approximately 10^{-6} g/g in the sample returned in the ALSRC. These results of the Apollo 11 ALSRC monitors led to improvements in cleaning procedures which produced flight hardware for Apollo 12 through 15 with an average of 10 to 100 ng/cm^2 of organic contamination. This 10 to 100 ng/cm^2 cleanliness level appears to be the

---

[7] The high resolution mass spectrometric data are presented as heteroatomic plots [25] with the masses plotted in methylene units. On the abscissa, each principal division marker corresponds to the saturated alkyl fragment (even-electron ion), for example C_nH_{2n+1}, with the number of carbon and hydrogen atoms given subsequently. Each principal division of the abscissa is further divided into seven units. The number of hydrogen atoms of an unsaturated or cyclic-fragment ion is obtained by subtracting the number of units (two hydrogen atoms) or half units from the $2_n + 1$ hydrogen atoms of the respective saturated principal division, C_nH_{2n+1}. Fragments with more than seven degrees of unsaturation are plotted with each principal division marker on the abscissa corresponding to the fragment ion C_nH_{2n-13}. Each principal division is again further divided into seven units, and the number of hydrogen atoms of a fragment ion is derived as just discussed.

TABLE 2–*Frequently encountered organic contaminants.*

Compound Name	Compound Structure	Apollo Mission	Source
1. Hydrocarbons	$C_nH_{2n\pm z}$ $n \cong 3$ to 35 $z \cong +2$ to -16	11 to 15	ubiquitous
2. Fatty acids	$C_nH_{2n}O_2$ (some C_nH_{2n-2},etc. O_2)	11 to 15	F-201 (LRL vacuum processing chamber) and ALSRC
Palmitic acid	$C_{16}H_{32}O_2$		
Stearic acid	$C_{18}H_{36}O_2$		
3. "Octoils"			
Dibutyl phthalate	$O-C_4H_9$ $O-C_4H_9$	11 to 15	ubiquitous
Dioctyl phthalate	$O-C_8H_{17}$ $O-C_8H_{17}$	11 to 15	ubiquitous
Dinonyl phthalate	$O-C_9H_{19}$ $O-C_9H_{19}$	12,14	ALSRC

TABLE 2–(Continued)

Compound Name	Compound Structure	Apollo Mission	Source
Didecyl phthalate		14	ALSRC
Dioctadecyl phthalate		14	ALSRC
4. Silicones		11 to 14	F-201, astronaut suit abrasion (boots)
5. Ethylene oxide polymers			
Trimethylene oxide		14	SNAP

p-dioxane

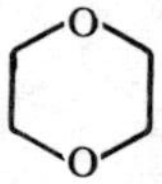

1,3,5,-trimethyl-2,4,6-trioxane

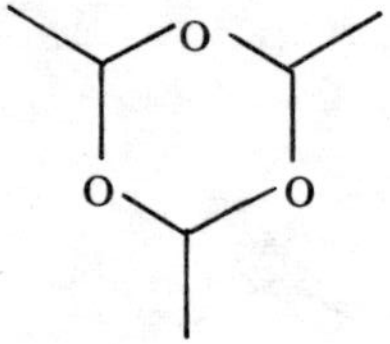

6. Orcinol

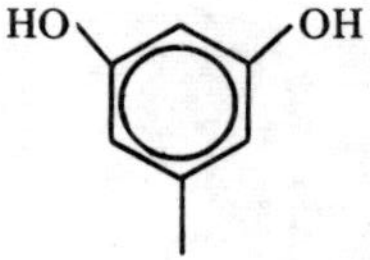

14   SNAP

7. Freons $C_2F_4Cl_2$ (eg)

11 to 14   NASA-WSTF cleaning residual

8. Phosphates (plasticizers)

Tributyl phosphate

$$C_4H_9-O-P(=O)(O-C_4H_9)-O-C_4H_9$$

11 to 12   F-201

Trihexyl phosphate

$$C_6H_{13}-O-P(=O)(O-C_6H_{13})-O-C_6H_{13}$$

11 to 12   ALSRC

TABLE 2–(*Continued*)

Compound Name	Compound Structure	Apollo Mission	Source
9. Oleamide		11 to 12	ALSRC
10. Cholesterol and others		11 to 15	ALSRC, York mesh monitor
11. Dibutyl sebacate		11,12	F-201
12. Dioctyl adipate		12	SESC lid[a] (Apollo 12)

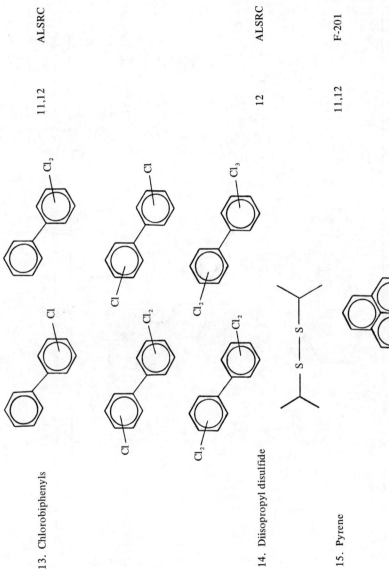

13. Chlorobiphenyls

11,12   ALSRC

14. Diisopropyl disulfide

12   ALSRC

15. Pyrene

11,12   F-201

TABLE 2–(*Continued*)

Compound Name	Compound Structure	Apollo Mission	Source
16. Tetrahydronaphthol		12	ALSRC
17. Ionol		11	curator polypropylene bottles
18. Teflon		11,12	nitrogen processing chamber

[a] SESC is the special environmental sample container used for storage of the "prime" organic sample. Attempts have been made on Apollo 12 through 15 to provide the cleanest possible sample by use of this special container.

lowest practical limit of York mesh type material and is undoubtedly partially due to aluminum oxide in the extracted residue weights.

The sterile nitrogen atmosphere processing (SNAP) line assembled at the LRL for Apollo 14 sample processing has introduced as much as 10 ppm of organic contamination to Ottawa sand monitors in the cleanest simulation [13]. These high levels are primarily due to the ethylene oxide sterilization of the cabinets and are comprised primarily of various polymerization products of ethylene oxide with minor amounts of dioctyl phthalate.

A listing of the most common and ubiquitous contaminants documented in this monitoring history [12-14] is given in Table 2, along with their sources. The Apollo mission for which the source is applicable is also listed. It should be noted that the number of compounds associated with the Apollo 14 and 15 missions is reduced significantly.

Conclusions

The primary purpose of this paper is to detail the contamination control procedures adopted to meet cleanliness requirements and to briefly present all the analytical evidence obtained throughout the program on potential contamination sources or contaminants. A summary of the terrestrial organic contaminants actually found in the lunar samples by the various laboratories participating in lunar sample analyses has been presented [10]. A contamination control plan was developed and implemented which eventually resulted in providing investigators with lunar samples containing less than 0.1 µg/g total terrestrial organic contamination. It should be noted that this is as low or lower than the experimental blanks usually obtained in organic geochemical research laboratories.

Acknowledgments

We thank Ellen Scott for technical assistance, A. L. Burlingame for use of the high resolution mass spectrometry facilities, the organic PET for the LRL monitoring, and I. D. Smith for assistance with the LM engine exhaust studies. The support under NASA Contracts NAS 9-9593 and NAS 9-7889 is gratefully acknowledged.

References

[1] Lunar Sample Preliminary Examination Team (LSPET), Science, Vol. 165, 1969, pp. 1211-1227.
[2] Lunar Sample Preliminary Examination Team (LSPET), Science, Vol. 167, 1970, pp. 1325-1339.
[3] Levinson, A. A., ed., Proceedings, Apollo 11 Lunar Science Conference, Vol. 2, Pergamon, New York, 1970, pp. 1757-1934.
[4] Levinson, A. A., ed., Proceedings, Second Lunar Science Conference, Geochimica et Cosmochimica Acta, Vol. 2, The MIT Press, Cambridge, Mass., 1971, pp. 1843-1931.
[5] Watkins, Carolyn, ed., Revised Abstracts, Third Lunar Science Conference, The Lunar Science Institute, Houston, Tex. 1972, Contribution No. 88.

[6] Heymann, D., ed., *Proceedings,* Third Lunar Science Conference, *Geochimica et Cosmochimica Acta,* Vol. 2, The MIT Press, Cambridge, Mass., 1972.
[7] Chamberlain, J. W. and Watkins, Carolyn, eds., *The Apollo 15 Lunar Samples,* The Lunar Science Institute, Houston, Tex., 1972.
[8] Lunar Sample Preliminary Examination Team (LSPET), *Science,* Vol. 173, 1971, pp. 681-693.
[9] Lunar Sample Preliminary Examination Team (LSPET), *Science,* Vol. 175, 1972, pp. 363-375.
[10] Flory, D. A. and Simoneit, B. R., *Space Life Sciences,* Vol. 3, 1972, pp. 457-468.
[11] Lunar Receiving Laboratory Cleaning Procedures for Contamination Control, MSC-03243, National Aeronautics and Space Administration-Manned Spacecraft Center, Houston, Tex., 1970.
[12] Simoneit, B. R. and Flory, D. A., "Apollo 11, 12 and 13 Organic Contamination Monitoring History," NASA-MSC special report, National Aeronautics and Space Administration-Manned Spacecraft Center, in press.
[13] Simoneit, B. R., "Appollo 14 Organic Contamination Monitoring History," University of California, Space Sciences Laboratory Report, in preparation, and NASA-MSC report, National Aeronautics and Space Administration-Manned Spacecraft Center, in preparation.
[14] Simoneit, B. R., "Apollo 15 Organic Contamination Monitoring History," University of California, Space Sciences Laboratory Report, in preparation, and NASA-MSC report, National Aeronautics and Space Administration-Manned Spacecraft Center, in preparation.
[15] Reynolds, M. A., "Apollo 14 and Apollo Gas Chromatographic Monitoring Results," NASA-MSC report, National Aeronautics and Space Administration-Manned Spacecraft Center, in preparation.
[16] Burlingame, A. L. in *Advances in Mass Spectrometry,* Vol. 4, E. Kendrick, ed., The Institute of Petroleum, London, 1968, p. 15.
[17] Burlingame, A. L. in *Recent Developments in Mass Spectroscopy,* K. Ogata and T. Hayakawa, eds., University of Tokyo Press, Tokyo, 1970, p. 104.
[18] Burlingame, A. L., Smith, D. H., Merren, T. O., and Olsen, R. W. in *Computers in Analytical Chemistry,* Vol. 4 in Progress in Analytical Chemistry Series, C. H. Orr and J. Norris, eds., Plenum Press, New York, 1970, p. 17.
[19] Burlingame, A. L., Holland, P., McFadden, W. H., Simoneit, B. R., Wilder, J. T., and Wszolek, P. C., "UCB Space Sciences Laboratory Organic Clean Room and Lunar Material Transfer Facilities," an internal report of the Space Sciences Laboratory, University of California, Berkeley, 1971.
[20] Burlingame, A. L., Holland, P., McFadden, W. H., Simoneit, B. R., Wilder, J. T., and Wszolek, P. C., "UCB Space Sciences Laboratory Simulation 3 Sand Transfer and Transfer of Apollo 14 SESC Lunar Material," an internal report of the Space Sciences Laboratory, University of California, Berkeley, 1971.
[21] Burlingame, A. L., Holland, P., McFadden, W. H., Simoneit, B. R., Wilder, J. T., and Wszolek, P. C., "UCB Space Sciences Laboratory Transfer of Pristine Lunar Material from Apollo 14 Rocks 14047 and 14049," University of California, Space Sciences Laboratory Report, Berkeley, 27 Sept. 1971.
[22] Simoneit, B. R., Wilder, J. T., and Wszolek, P. C., "UCB Space Sciences Laboratory Organic Clean Room and Lunar Material Transfer Facilities. The Transfer of Pristine Lunar Material from the Apollo 15 SESC 15012 and SESC 15013," University of California, Space Sciences Laboratory Report, Berkeley, 10 June 1972.
[23] Simoneit, B. R., Burlingame, A. L., Flory, D. A., and Smith, I. D., *Science,* Vol. 166, 1969, pp. 733-738.
[24] Flory, D. A., Simoneit, B. R., Burlingame, A. L., and Smith, I. D., "Experimental Determination of Potential Lunar Surface Organic Contamination in the Lunar Module Descent Engine Exhaust," Technical Report R-389, National Aeronautics and Space Administration, 1972.
[25] Burlingame, A. L. and Smith, D. H., *Tetrahedron,* Vol. 24, 1968, p. 5749.

P. C. Wszolek,[1] P. T. Holland,[1] W. H. McFadden,[1] A. L. Burlingame,[1] J. T. Wilder,[1] and B. R. Simoneit[1]

Monitoring Systems for Evaluation of Terrestrial Contamination in a Lunar Sample Transfer Facility

REFERENCE: Wszolek, P. C., Holland, P. T., McFadden, W. H., Burlingame, A. L., Wilder, J. T., and Simoneit, B. R., "Monitoring Systems for Evaluation of Terrestrial Contamination in a Lunar Sample Transfer Facility," *Analytical Methods Developed for Application to Lunar Samples Analyses, ASTM STP 539*, American Society for Testing and Materials, 1973, pp. 35–55.

ABSTRACT: A lunar sample transfer facility has been assembled in our laboratory to maintain a high level of lunar sample integrity and purity with respect to terrestrial water, terrestrial organic and bio-organic compounds, and other terrestrial contaminants. The facility consists of two tandem glove boxes and an entrance vacuum antechamber all of which are located in a certified class 100 clean room (100 particles/ft^3)

Nitrogen gas from liquid nitrogen is circulated through the glove boxes at a rate of about 0.5 ft^3/min. It is purified by passing it through a bed of finely divided copper and then molecular sieves. A stainless steel tubing analysis line connects the boxes with three monitoring systems. A continuous flow of nitrogen gas is maintained in the analysis line by a small diaphragm pump situated at the exit of the line. A valving arrangement allows the sampling of either the inlet or outlet nitrogen stream, to or from the glove boxes. The level of contaminants in the glove box atmosphere is assessed by three monitoring systems: (1) Water content is determined using an electrolytic cell water analyzer (duPont-CEC Instruments, Model 26-303) which can detect 0.1 ppm of water in the nitrogen stream. (2) Permanent gases (oxygen, carbon dioxide, carbon monoxide, menthane, etc.) are analyzed by a Varian-Aerograph trace gas analyzer (Model 1732-20) fitted with dual ultrasensitive helium ionization detectors which are sensitive to all atoms and molecules except neon. For most gases detection limits are in the 10 ppb range. A 20 ft by 1/8-in. stainless steel column packed with 5 Å molecular sieve is used to determine argon, oxygen, methane, and carbon monoxide. The other column is 10 ft by 1/8-in. stainless steel packed with Poropak Q and is used to determine CO_2 and C_2

[1] Spectroscopist, postgraduate research chemist, specialist, research chemist, spectroscopist, and specialist respectively, University of California, Berkeley, Space Sciences Laboratory, Berkeley, Calif. 94720.

and C_3 hydrocarbons. (3) Low volatility organic matter is monitored primarily by bubbling the glove box exhaust gas through dichloromethane in a gas washing bottle cooled to −30 to −60° C. Auxiliary monitoring consists of exposing sintered aluminum plaques in the glove box atmosphere and subsequently extracting them with dichloromethane to release absorbed contaminants. During the simulated distribution of lunar material, still another monitor was available, that is, the Ottawa sand which was manipulated and transferred in lieu of the lunar material and which was subsequently extracted with dichloromethane.[2] Extracts from each of these monitors were concentrated at 0°C to retain as much of the volatile components as possible. Analysis of the extracts is achieved by capillary gas liquid chromatography, (GLC) using a hydrogen flame detector whose minimum detectable level per component is 0.5 ng. The C_{10} to C_{30} hydrocarbon range is covered by the GLC conditions used. High resolution mass spectrometry for total extract analysis and gas chromatography/mass spectrometry (GC/MS) for individual component identification are also available when needed. Efficiencies of various steps in the analytical scheme were determined by control experiments. Monitoring results will be presented for several periods including simulated distributions of lunar material, distribution of Apollo 14 and 15 special environment sample container (SESC) and distribution of Apollo 14 rocks 14047 and 14049. The level of individual permanent gases was usually a few parts per million (ppm) or lower. Low volatility organic contamination was at the parts per billion (ppb) level or lower.

KEY WORDS: terrestrial contamination, glove boxes, moisture meters, gas analysis, gas chromatography, mass spectrometry, lunar analysis

Throughout the preparations and actual Apollo missions, a major effort has been devoted toward developing return and sample handling procedures which will preserve the integrity of the lunar sample, both for immediate allocation for scientific study as well as curatorial preservation of pristine material.

Due to the many constraints on handling and preliminary examination of the lunar samples, preservation of their organic and anhydrous integrity has been the most difficult aspect to achieve. The quarantine protocols have augered against achieving a lunar sample uncontaminated with terrestrial organic matter and moisture.

Experience with the Apollo 11 and 12 missions and continued constraints at the Lunar Receiving Laboratory (LRL) dictated that it was not practicable to maintain ultraorganic cleanliness for the entire suite of returned lunar material, and hence the collection of a special sample sealed in a special environment sample container (SESC) was implemented for the Apollo 14 and subsequent missions.

After Apollo 12, the science directorate at the National Aeronautics and Space Administration-Manned Spacecraft Center (NASA-MSC), with the advice of the lunar sample analysis planning team, took steps to develop one facility for ultraorganic clean handling where the necessary detailed microanalytical

---

[2] The exposed sand was also analyzed for amino acid contamination by other research groups performing these analyses on lunar samples.

capability existed and could be mobilized for monitoring. Such a lunar sample transfer facility has been established in our laboratory to maintain a high level of lunar sample integrity and purity with respect to terrestrial water, terrestrial organic and bio-organic compounds, and other terrestrial contaminants. The facility consists of two tandem glove boxes and an entrance vacuum ante-chamber, all of which are located in a class 100 clean room (certified at <50 particles/ft^3). This report will describe the monitoring systems we have used to evaluate the contamination levels of water, permanent gases, and lower volatility organic compounds in the glove box atmosphere. The monitoring procedures developed at NASA-MSC have been oriented toward the analyses for the more nonvolatile organic materials ($>C_{15}$) [1, 2].[3] For our facility new monitoring procedures were devised to allow quantitation of the possible more volatile contaminants.

Experimental Procedures

Glove Box Atmosphere

The schematic diagram in Fig. 1 shows the design of the glove boxes and the flow of gas through them. The inert atmosphere for the dry box system is usually nitrogen vaporized from a liquid nitrogen tank (area 1 in Fig. 1). The gas is purified by passing it through finely divided copper to remove residual oxygen, and molecular sieve X 13 to remove carbon monoxide (CO), carbon dioxide (CO_2), water (H_2O), and other impurities (item 3 in Fig. 1). The gas is directed first into the second glove box and then into the first glove box (areas 6 and 7 in Fig. 1). A bypass (item 14 in Fig. 1) provides a purge of the antechamber when necessary. The exit from the first box to atmosphere is protected by a ground glass check valve (item 9 in Fig. 1) and finally by a trap of molecular sieve X 13 (item 10 in Fig. 1).

The antechamber has a vacuum manifold that is used to evacuate air when materials are placed in it prior to entering the glove box area. Pumping is accomplished by using a Varian sorption pump (item 15 in Fig. 1), thus eliminating the possibility of pump oil contamination.

Bypass sample valves (items 4 and 8 in Fig. 1) have been installed at the entrance and in Glove Box 2 to permit sampling of the gas so that it can be monitored for CO, CO_2 O_2, low volatility. organics, etc. The analysis or monitoring line (items 4 and 8 through 11c in Fig. 1) consists of 1/8-in. stainless steel tubing with a small diaphragm pump situated at the exit of the line to maintain a continuous flow of nitrogen gas. The flow rate through the line is about 200 cm^3/min or about 1/2 to 1 percent of the total flow through the

---

[3] The italic numbers in brackets refer to the list of references appended to this paper.

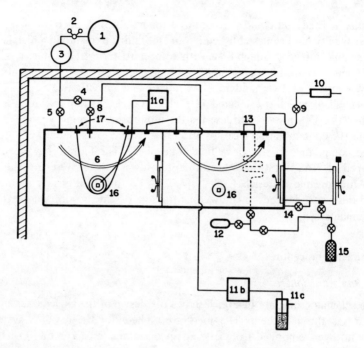

FIG. 1–*Schematic of the gas flow in the glove boxes:* (1) *liquid* N_2; (2) *gas flow regulator;* (3) *purifier-molecular sieve, fine copper;* (4) *entrance line sample valve;* (5) *dry box isolation valve;* (6) *gas flow through second box;* (7) *gas flow through first box;* (8) *Box 2 sample valve;* (9) *check valve;* (10) *molecular sieve;* (11) *monitors:* (a) H_2O, (b) *volatile organics by GC,* (c) *low volatility organics;* (12) *gas sample bottle;* (13) *vacuum line;* (14) *purge line—antechamber;* (15) *sorption pump;* (16) *stud for socket wrench;* and (17) *liquid nitrogen refrigeration coil. (One coil in each box. Not illustrated for Box 1.)*

glove boxes. An alternative analysis line has been set up for monitoring the exhaust gas from Glove Box 1 (7 in Fig. 1). This line is not illustrated in Fig. 1, but it would extend from item 9 through 11*b* and 11*c*.

An electrolytic moisture analyzer on a separate analysis line, (item 11*a* in Fig. 1) (duPont Instruments, Model 26-303) can detect 0.1 ppm of H_2O in the gas stream. Permanent gases such as CO, CO_2, methane (CH_4), ethane (C_2H_6), etc. are monitored using a Varian trace gas analyzer (item 11*b* in Fig. 1), Model 1732-20 gas chromatography (GC) unit equipped with a metastable helium detector. The minimum detectable limit for most gases is less than 0.01 ppm. Low volatility organic matter is monitored primarily by bubbling the glove box exhaust gas through dichloromethane in a gas washing bottle (item 11*c* in Fig. 1) cooled to −40 to −60°C.

Water Monitoring

The moisture analyzer accomplishes its analysis by continuously and quantitatively absorbing and electrolyzing all water in the sample stream. The water is absorbed on the thin film of phosphorus pentoxide deposited between the two electrodes of the electrolytic cell. Voltage applied to these electrodes causes them to be highly polarized, and electrolysis of the absorbed water into hydrogen and oxygen results.

Flow of the sample gas is kept constant by using a flow controller, and thus the indicated current is proportional only to the water concentration. The instrument has a dynamic range of 1 to 1000 ppm of water by volume. Its response time is rated at 30 s or less to a large step change, well within our requirements. The accuracy of the moisture monitor is ±5 percent of full scale of the indicated reading.

Volatile Gas Analysis

Monitoring of the glove box atmosphere for volatile gases is performed by a Varian-Aerograph trace gas analyzer, Model 1732-20 (item 11b in Fig. 1), equipped with dual solid adsorbent columns and helium ionization detectors. The detectors are extremely sensitive to all permanent gases except neon. Under favorable conditions, the detection limit for hydrogen (H_2), argon, nitrogen (N_2), and CO is 10 ppb, and 1 ppb for CO_2, O_2, and CH_4. Helium passing from the chromatographic columns is excited to the metastable state (energy level = 19.8 eV) within the detectors. All permanent gases except neon are in turn ionized and produce a positive increase in detector current. An exponential dilution flask is used to calibrate the detectors over the range 0.1 to 100 ppm, or higher if necessary, using aliquots of the various pure gases. Their response is essentially linear over this range.

A 20 ft by 1/8-in. stainless steel column, packed with 5 Å molecular sieve is used to separate H_2, argon, O_2, N_2, CH_4, and CO. The first five components are separated at an isothermal column temperature of 50°C. Figures 2 and 3 show typical separations. The retention time of CO is excessive at this temperature, and this component is determined separately at 110°C. The other column is 10 ft by 1/8-in. stainless steel packed with Porapak Q and is used to separate CO_2, C_2, and C_3 hydrocarbons. A typical separation is shown in Fig. 4. The column temperature is 50°C isothermal in this case as well.

Sample gas from the monitoring line continuously flows through one of the two loops of the sampling valve on the trace gas analyzer. Helium carrier gas flows through the other loop. A simple rotation of the valve injects the sample gas by simply switching the configuration of the two loops. Thus, a fixed portion of the sample gas, 0.25 ml, is flushed onto the columns. The sample is

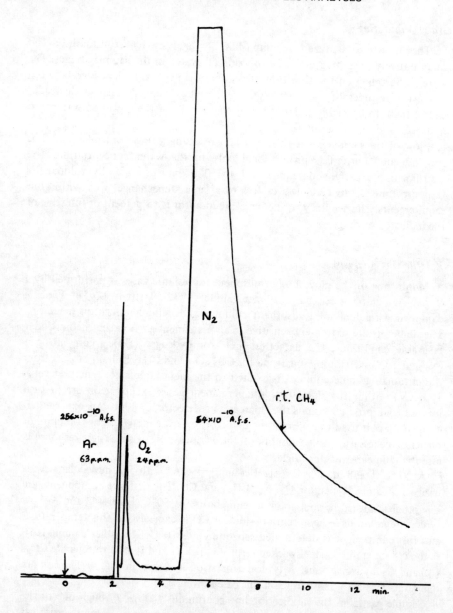

FIG. 2—*Gas chromatogram of purge nitrogen from glove boxes. Column: 20 ft by 1/8-in. stainless steel packed with 5 A molecular sieve; helium flow rate: 60 ml/min; column temperature: 50° C isothermal.*

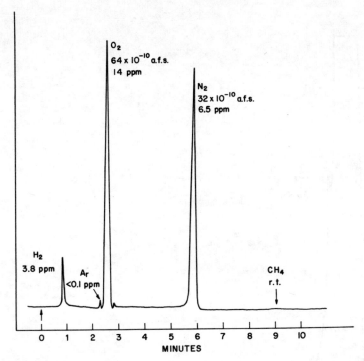

FIG. 3—*Gas chromatogram of purge helium from glove boxes. Conditions same as in Fig. 2.*

split 50/50 immediately before entering the columns. Carrier gas flow through both columns is 50 to 60 ml/min.

Lower Volatility Organic Contaminants

Our monitoring for organic compounds seeks to establish the level of contamination in the glove box atmosphere as well as on any surfaces that the lunar sample may contact. To sample the glove box atmosphere for organic compounds the gas from the monitoring line is passed through a gas washing bottle (11c in Fig. 1) filled with 200-ml dichloromethane and cooled to −40 to −60°C. The inner glass tube of the gas-washing bottle is submerged in the dichloromethane (CH_2Cl_2), and the end of the tube is a glass frit which disperses the gas into a fine stream of bubbles which ascend through the solvent. We will refer to this device as the "bubbler." It is illustrated in Fig. 5. A dry ice/acetone bath can be used for cooling, but, for extended monitoring periods, we find it convenient to use a Vacumetrics Cryocool cooling coil submerged in an alcohol bath because it requires no attention to maintain −60°C. This low

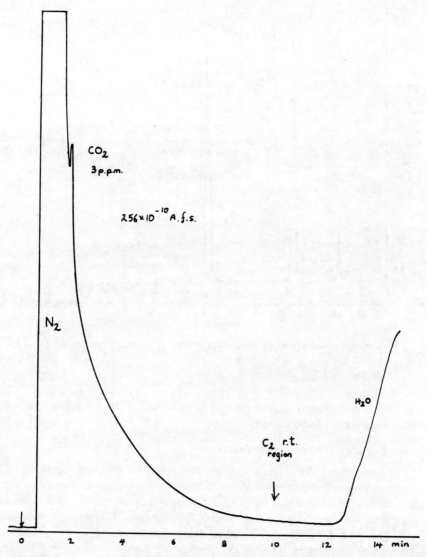

FIG. 4—*Gas chromatogram of purge nitrogen from glove boxes. Column: 10 ft by 1/8-in. stainless steel packed with Poropak Q; helium flow rate: 60 ml/min; and column temperature: 50°C isothermal.*

FIG. 5—*Gas-washing bottle or bubbler filled with dichloromethane used for monitoring for lower volatility organic contaminants. Cooling bath is a Vacumetrics Cryocool refrigeration coil immersed in alcohol.*

temperature minimizes evaporation of the solvent as well as any of the trapped contaminants and aids in trapping the contaminants.

A simple experiment was designed to get some idea about the efficiency of the bubbler. Known amounts of standards were placed in a glass trap having an inlet and an outlet and a volume of about 200 ml. The trap outlet was connected to the inlet of the gas washing bottle which was about 80 percent full with CH_2Cl_2, that is, 200 ml. Air was flushed through the inlet of the trap and through the whole system at 100 cm^3/min for 1 h. The gas washing bottle was cooled to about $-40°C$ with a dry ice/acetone bath. The CH_2Cl_2 solution was then concentrated as described next and the extract analyzed by gas liquid chromatography (GLC). The results of the control experiment are shown in Table 1. Several points can be taken from the data. One can detect microgram quantities of organic contaminants provided that they have sufficiently high vapor pressures to be swept out of the container into the CH_2Cl_2. For example, decalin and methyl laurate were recovered with relatively good yields at the 1 μg level, but diisobutyl phthalate, which has a much lower vapor pressure, was not. Furthermore, methyl palmitate, which also has a relatively low vapor pressure, was only recovered to the extent of about 1 percent from 100 μg of material. As might be expected, the best yields or efficiencies of recovery were obtained for methyl laurate and hexadecane. These compounds of intermediate vapor pressure are in a maximum recovery range where vapor pressure is high enough for detection but not so high as to be readily lost by evaporation from the CH_2Cl_2 trap.

Ottawa sand, previously baked at $1100°C$, has been used during simulations of lunar sample transfers to assess the danger of contamination arising from surfaces which the actual sample will contact directly. The sand can also adsorb contaminants from the atmosphere. It is manipulated much as the lunar sample is with various glove box tools and is transferred to appropriate containers. After exposure in this fashion, the sand is extracted with dichloromethane in an ultrasonic tank to remove any possible contaminants for subsequent analysis.

TABLE 1—Gas sampling procedure recovery effieiency.

Standard	Total Amount Used, μg	Amount Recovered, μg
Cis-decalin, $C_{10}H_{18}$	0.9	0.2
Decane, $C_{10}H_{22}$	10.8	0.8
Methyl laurate, $C_{13}H_{26}O_2$	1.4	0.5
Hexadecane, $C_{16}H_{34}$	9.8	3.1
Diisobutyl phthalate, $C_{16}H_{22}O_4$	1.2	nd[a]
Methyl palmitate, $C_{17}H_{34}O_2$	104.6	0.9

[a] nd = not detected.

We have also experimented with another type of organic monitor, the so-called alumina plaques, but they have been of questionable value. These plaques were thought to provide an adsorbent matrix for exposure in the glove boxes, but results from controlled atmosphere experiments as well as actual exposure in the glove boxes have been negative. Like the sand, the plaques were fired at $1100°C$ before exposure for cleaning and activation, and they were extracted with CH_2Cl_2 after exposure.

The plaque extract, the sand extract, and the gas-wash solution are all concentrated as follows: the sand extracts are cooled to $0°C$ (ice bath) and the CH_2Cl_2 is stripped off with a water aspirator vacuum on a Büchi rotary evaporator. Solvent vapors are trapped with a liquid nitrogen trap. The solution is concentrated to about 1 to 2 ml in 1 h. Sometimes a "keeper" consisting of 20 μl of heptane is added, and the final concentration to a total volume of 10 to 20 μl is carried out with a stream of pure nitrogen gas at $0°C$. The ice bath temperature is used to minimize evaporation losses of the more volatile contaminants ($<C_{15}$) by lowering their vapor pressure. Since the CH_2Cl_2 still has an appreciable vapor pressure at this temperature, it can be stripped off in a reasonable amount of time.

All monitor extract residues and the corresponding control extract residues were analyzed with a Perkin-Elmer Model 900 gas chromatograph using a hydrogen flame ionization detector. A 100 ft by 0.03-in. inside diameter stainless steel capillary column coated with OV-101 was used for all analyses. The temperature was held at $45°C$ for 12.5 min and then programmed to $235°C$ at $2°C/min$. The injector and manifold temperatures were 220 and $300°C$, respectively. Minimum detectability per peak is about 0.5 ng for most organic compounds. These analytical conditions cover approximately the C_{10} to C_{30} hydrocarbon range.

A modified injector port was used to reduce injector septum bleed which is often a serious problem in temperature programmed gas chromatographic runs at the nanogram sensitivity level. The bleeding from the septum can produce peaks considerably more intense than the sample being analyzed, and, thus, the gas chromatographic analysis is either confusing or worthless. The injector port we are using is described elsewhere [3]. It accomplishes its task by insulating the septum from the elevated injector temperatures by providing surfaces for loss of heat by radiation between the septum and the injector chamber where samples are vaporized. A 3-in. syringe needle is employed to ensure that the sample is deposited in the hot zone.

Usually, only about 2 percent of the total extract residue, that is, about 0.2 μl out of 10 μl, is expended for gas chromatographic analysis. This is sufficient to determine the quantities and distribution pattern for the contaminants. The remainder of the residue may then be used for high resolution mass spectrometric analysis of the total mixture. High resolution mass spectrometry

(HRMS) information can be used to identify individual contaminants or at least indicate their compound class. The HRMS analyses are carried out at a dynamic resolution of 10 000 using a GEC-AEI MS-902 mass spectrometer on-line to an XDS Sigma-7 computer. The samples are introduced via a ceramic direct inlet probe into the ion source,[4] operated at 200 to 220°C with an ionizing current of 500 μA and an ionizing voltage of 50 V. The scan rate is 16 per decade with a clock rate of 24 kHz. Selected HRMS data can then be presented as heteratomic plots [7] for the chemist's convenience.

Results and Applications

The monitoring systems just described have been used during preparations for and simulations of lunar sample transfers and during the actual distribution of the Apollo 14 SESC, lunar rocks 14047 and 14049, and the Apollo 15 SESC. The results of all of this monitoring have been detailed elsewhere[8-11], but some specific applications, examples, and typical values will be given here.

Water Analyses

During preparations for the distribution of the Apollo 14 SESC, data obtained from manipulations in the boxes indicated that under standard conditions it would not be possible to maintain a low (less than 20 ppm) water level while working with the Neoprene gloves. This is clearly due to the fact that the Neoprene gloves are themselves a significant source of water when manipulated, and values ranging from 50 to 160 ppm are commonly observed.

In order to effect some removal of this water in the active area, a small (8-in.-diameter) stainless steel coil was put in each glove box so that liquid nitrogen can be circulated through the coil (see Fig. 1). This cooling device resulted in a significant improvement as is indicated by the following typical set of data:

Probe Position in Box 2	Water Level, ppm
Inlet	3 to 4
Static	15 to 20
Gloves in use (Neoprene)	60 to 120
Gloves in use with liquid N_2	15 to 50
Static with liquid N_2	6 to 8

Light Gas Monitoring

A summary of the results obtained during the distribution of the Apollo 14 SESC is given in Table 2 for light gases.

---

[4] A glass distillation tube is used for introducing volatile organic compounds from a dilute solution in dichloromethane. The procedure used is described in Ref 6.

The relative stability of the values for argon, oxygen, and carbon dioxide indicate that there were no gross leaks of air into the boxes or any significant adsorption of air on tools and containers that were brought into the glove boxes through the antechamber. All carbon containing gases were very low in concentration.

During the allocation of Apollo 15 SESC material, the inert atmosphere of the glove boxes was changed to helium at the request of investigators who wanted to minimize the sample's exposure to nitrogen. Air leaks were, therefore, especially critical during this time and did occur on several occasions. One such occasion is illustrated in a portion of the log recorded for the Apollo 15 SESC distribution[11]:

Date	Time			H_2O (ppm)
3/30/72	1032	(18)	Monitoring of light gases H_2, 2.9 ppm; Ar, <0.1 ppm; O_2, 6.0 ppm; N_2, 8.0 ppm	
	1035	(19)	WMcF in Box 1	
	1036	(20)	Close vacuum chamber valve and pump on gas sample bottle	2.0
	1037	(21)	Vent vacuum chamber	
	1040	(22)	Monitoring of light gases H_2, 4.1 ppm; Ar, <0.1 ppm; O_2, ~20 ppm N_2, ~30 ppm	
	1042	(23)	Transfer BTC,[a] etc., to Box 1 after He venting	3.0
	1044	(24)	Cut off Teflon bag, return bag to antechamber, and close the door	4.4
	1045	(25)	Attach BTC to the vacuum line, close gas sample bottle valve, open sorption pump to the line; BTC is tight	4.3
	1046	(26)	Monitoring of light gases H_2, 3.1 ppm; Ar, 4.4 ppm; O_2, ~ 130 ppm, N_2, 600 ppm	

[a] BTC = bolt top can.

The dramatic increase in the O_2, N_2, and argon levels from the time of the first monitor shown at 1032 compared with the values obtained at 1046 can be attributed to an inadequate pump down of the antechamber or air trapped in the Teflon bag. Continuous light gas monitoring during allocation brought these leaks to the immediate attention of the personnel involved within seconds or

TABLE 2–*Light gas and water monitoring, Apollo 14 SESC sample allocation.*

	Static Value, ppm	Gloves in Use, ppm
Argon		range 40 to 70
Oxygen	1	2 to 4
CO_2	0.1	0.15
CO	<0.1	<0.1
CH_4	<0.1	<0.1
C_2 to C_4 hydrocarbons	<0.1	<0.1
Water	20.0	30 to 70^a (liquid N_2 in cool coil)

[a] SESC closed until value less than 50.

minutes after they occurred. Decisions could then be made as to the cause of the leak and what change(s) should be made in the protocol for allocation. Once the exact concentration of N_2 and O_2 were determined, an estimate could be made for the time when the glove box atmosphere would return to normal since the flow rate of fresh helium through the boxes is known.

Low Volatility Organic Monitoring

Data in Table 3 represent the monitoring results associated with the Apollo 14 SESC allocation, and Fig. 6 shows the GC traces obtained from the corresponding bubbler solutions. Compare these traces with the trace for the blank or unexposed bubbler in Fig. 7. Pre-SESC Bubbler 1 sampled the exhaust gases three days before the SESC transfer. A total of 1.9 μg or 0.6 ppb of organic material in the C_{10} to C_{12} hydrocarbon region of the chromatogram was detected. No significant change is observed in SESC Bubbler 2 (next day)

TABLE 3–*Quantitative estimate of total low volatility organic material (Apollo 14 SESC transfer).*

Monitor	Sampling Time, h	Amount
Aluminum plaques	26	nd^a, <0.1 ppb (weight contamination)/(weight plaques)
Pre-SESC Bubbler 1	23	1.9 μg, 0.6 ppb (weight contamination)/(weight air)
Pre-SESC Bubbler 2	20	1.2 μg, 0.4 ppb (weight contamination)/(weight air)
SESC Bubbler	29	0.3 μg, 0.1 ppb (weight contamination)/(weight air)
Post-SESC Bubbler	16	0.5 μg, 0.2 ppb (weight contamination)/(weight air)

[a] nd = not detected.

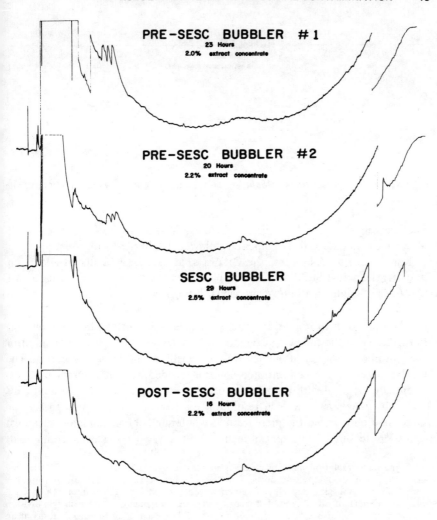

FIG. 6—*Gas chromatograms of extract concentrates from bubblers exposed during distribution of the Apollo 14 SESC. Column: 100 ft by 0.03 in. stainless steel coated with OV-101; helium: 5 psi; injector: 220°C; manifold: 300°C; column temperature: 45°C isothermal for 12 min then programmed to 235°C at 2°C/min.*

except that the amount of contamination had dropped slightly to 1.2 μg or 0.4 ppb. One extra peak appears at the end of this chromatogram with the same retention time as the peak observed in the same region of the blank chromatogram (Fig. 7). The level of organic contamination indicated for the SESC bubbler dropped further to 0.3 μg or 0.1 ppb. This bubbler sampled the exhaust gas during the day preceding the SESC transfer and during the actual

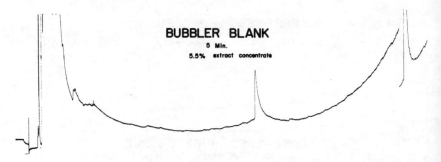

FIG. 7–*Gas chromatogram of bubbler blank (exposed for only 5 min). Conditions same as in Fig. 6.*

SESC distribution. The Post-SESC Bubbler indicated a total of 0.5 μg or 2 ppb of organic material for the 16 h period following the SESC distribution.

For comparison purposes, the Ottawa sand used in a simulated allocation prior to the actual SESC distribution picked up 0.4 μg of contaminants or 2.1 ppb (weight contamination/weight sand) eluting in the C_{28} to C_{30} hydrocarbon region of the chromatogram.

The value of high resolution mass spectrometry in our monitoring scheme is illustrated with the following example. A bubbler solution was used to monitor the glove boxes shortly after they were originally set up in our laboratory. The GLC analysis of the concentrated solution yielded a chromatogram that was essentially identical with that for the background at the level of maximum GLC sensitivity. However, the high resolution mass spectral data[5] (Fig. 8) for the same solution revealed the presence of a whole suite of contaminants. The most significant feature is the extent of high molecular weight oxygenated compounds

---

[5] The high resolution mass spectrum is presented as heteroatomic plots [7] with the masses plotted in methylene units. On the abscissa, each principal division marker corresponds to the saturated alkyl fragment (even-electron ion), for example, C_nH_{2n+1}, with the number of carbon and hydrogen atoms given subsequently. Each principal division of the abscissa is further divided into seven units. The number of hydrogen atoms of an unsaturated or cyclic-fragment ion is obtained by subtracting the number of units (two hydrogen atoms) or half units from the $2n + 1$ hydrogen atoms of the respective saturated principal division, C_nH_{2n+1}. The second, fourth and sixth plots in Fig. 8 show fragments which have more than seven degrees of unsaturation. Each principal division marker corresponds to the fragment ion C_nH_{2n-14}. Each principal division is again further divided into seven units and the number of hydrogen atoms of a fragment ion is derived as just discussed. The origin of the abscissas is the same m/e ratio for each plot; thus, the nominal masses from plot to plot lie directly above one another and a superposition of the plots would yield a "low" resolution mass spectrum of the sample. The nominal masses are indicated in 50 mass unit intervals below the carbon/hydrogen ratio scale. All plots are normalized to a base peak (usually the base peak of the entire spectrum, unless otherwise specified) on the relative intensity scale. In order to make high mass, low intensity features of the spectrum observable, the whole spectrum or any region thereof can be multiplied by a scale factor. This factor is indicated by /×00 at the point of scale expansion.

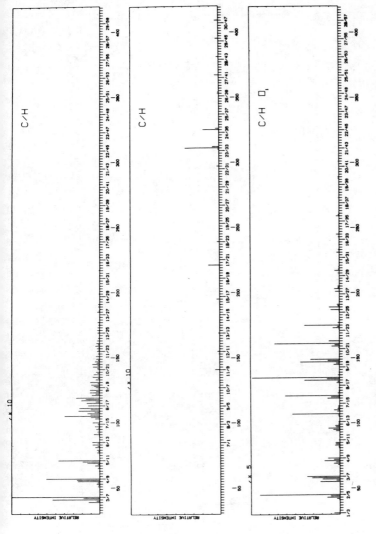

FIG. 8—*High resolution mass spectrum of the residue from a bubbler exposed during preparations for the distribution of Apollo 14 SESC. The spectrum is presented as a series of heteroatomic plots [7].*

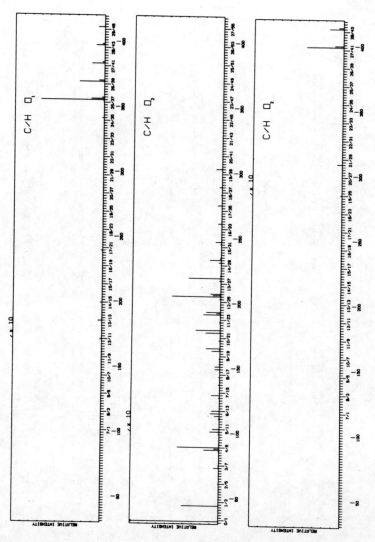

FIG. 8—*Continued.*

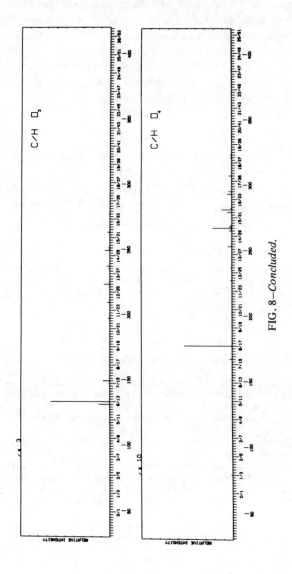

FIG. 8—*Concluded.*

as shown in the C/H O, C/H O$_2$, C/H O$_3$, C/H O$_4$ plots in Fig. 8. These ion peaks appear to be possible contaminants (for example, antioxidants and plasticizers) from the Neoprene gloves used in the glove boxes. Such compounds would be quite polar and hence not observed in the gas chromatogram. A subsequent extraction was made on one of these gloves and a high resolution mass spectrum run on the concentrated extract. Although the glove extract was far more complex, a considerable correspondence could be observed with the mass spectrum obtained from the bubbler concentrate. The source of this contaminant was thus considered confirmed. Contamination from this source decreased with time after the initial outgassing.

Conclusions

The monitoring systems just described provide a good, comprehensive record for the overall exposure of the transferred lunar material to terrestrial water, permanent gases, and low volatility organic contaminants. Real-time information is available during sample transfers for water and the permanent gases.

Acknowledgments

We wish to thank E. Yang, A. Sadorra, and E. Scott for technical assistance and the National Aeronautics and Space Administration, Grant NGR-05-003-435, for financial support.

References

[1] Simoneit, B. R. and Flory, D. A., "Apollo 11, 12, and 13 Organic Contamination Monitoring History," NASA report, National Aeronautics and Space Administration, in press.

[2] Simoneit, B. R., "Apollo 14 Organic Contamination Monitoring History," NASA-MSC report, National Aeronautics and Space Administration-Manned Spacecraft Center, Houston, Tex., in press.

[3] Tucknott, O. G. and Williams, A. A., Analytical Chemistry, Vol. 41, Dec. 1969, p. 2086.

[4] Burlingame, A. L. in Advances in Mass Spectrometry, Vol. 4, E. Kendrick, ed., The Institute of Petroleum, London, 1968, p. 15.

[5] Burlingame, A. L., Smith, D. H., Merren, T. O., and Olsen, R. W. in Computers in Analytical Chemistry, Vol. 4 in Progress in Analytical Chemistry series, C. H. Orr and J. Norris, eds., Plenum Press, New York, 1970, p. 17.

[6] Biemann, K., Mass Spectrometry, Organic Chemical Applications, McGraw-Hill, New York, 1962, pp. 28-30.

[7] Burlingame, A. L. and Smith, D. H., Tetrahedron, Vol. 24, 1968, p. 5749.

[8] Burlingame, A. L., Holland, P. T., McFadden, W. H., Simoneit, B. R., Wilder, J. T., and Wszolek, P. C., "UCB Space Sciences Laboratory Organic Clean Room and Lunar Material Transfer Facilities," Space Sciences Laboratory Report, University of California, Berkeley, 18 May 1971.

[9] Burlingame, A. L. and Smith, D. H., "UCB Space Sciences Laboratory Simulation 3 Sand Transfer and Transfer of Apollo 14 SESC Lunar Material," Space Sciences Laboratory Report, University of California, Berkeley, 17 June 1971.

[*10*] Burlingame, A. L., Smith, D. H., Holland, P. T., McFadden, W. H., Simoneit, B. R., Wilder, J. T., and Wszolek, P. C., "UCB Space Sciences Laboratory Transfer of Pristine Lunar Material from Apollo 14 Rocks 14047 and 14049," Space Sciences Laboratory report, University of California, Berkeley, 27 Sept. 1971.

[*11*] Simoneit, B. R., Wilder, J. T., and Wszolek, P. C., "UCB Space Sciences Laboratory Organic Clean Room and Lunar Material Transfer Facilities. The Transfer of Pristine Lunar Material from the Apollo 15 SESC 15012 and SESC 15013," Space Sciences Laboratory report, University of California, Berkeley, 10 June 1972.

Colin Barker [1] *and M. A. Sommer* [1]

Mass Spectrometric Analysis of the Volatiles Released by Heating or Crushing Rocks

REFERENCE: Barker, Colin and Sommer, M. A.,"Mass Spectrometric Analysis of the Volatiles Released by Heating or Crushing Rocks," *Analytical Methods Developed for Application to Lunar Samples Analyses, ASTM STP 539,* American Society for Testing and Materials, 1973, pp. 56–70.

ABSTRACT: The volatiles trapped in rocks can be released either by heating or by crushing. Unfortunately crushing generates new, clean surfaces which adsorb chemically active gases and thus change both the amount and composition of the evolved gases. For quantitative analysis the volatiles were released by heating 0.1-g samples in fused silica tubes at temperatures up to 1200°C. The evolved volatiles were separated into two fractions by fractional freezing. Volatiles which were not condensed in a liquid nitrogen-cooled trap (hydrogen, carbon monoxide, methane, nitrogen, helium, etc.) were mixed with a known amount of argon internal standard and leaked into a calibrated E.A.I. QUAD 1110 mass spectrometer for analysis. The condensable volatiles (water, carbon dioxide, higher hydrocarbons) were subsequently evaporated and analyzed in the same way. The analog output from the mass spectrometer was fed to a digital integrator which printed the areas of the peaks on a teletype and simultaneously punched a paper tape. The tape was later transmitted over a telephone line to a time-shared computer for data processing.

KEY WORDS: lunar analysis, volatiles, lunar rock, rocks, mass spectrometers, computers, crushing, heating

Naturally occurring silicate melts (magmas) contain volatile components which profoundly influence their behavior. The viscosity, freezing range, crystallization sequence, and composition and texture of the mineral products all depend on the amount and composition of the volatiles. In spite of their importance very little is known about them. This is due in part to the insurmountable problem of sampling magmas directly. Several indirect methods are available, for example, the volatiles released during volcanic activity are

[1] Associate professor, Chemistry Department and graduate student, Department of Earth Sciences, respectively, University of Tulsa, Tulsa, Okla. 74104.

derived from a magmatic source. Unfortunately these volatiles are almost certainly contaminated with ground water and atmospheric gases and also suffer from the more serious problem that they correspond to the composition of magmatic volatiles at only one point in geologic time and can provide no data for the volatiles released in the past. An alternative approach is to study the rocks which crystallized from the magmas since these solid products can trap small samples of the volatiles associated with the parent melt. Although there are difficulties in relating the composition of the volatiles in rocks to those present in the melt at the time of crystallization, this does provide a potential method for estimating the composition of the volatiles associated with magmas generated up to about 3.5 billion years ago. This approach is equally valid for terrestrial and lunar samples.

Apparatus

Introduction

The volatiles trapped in rocks and minerals can be released either by heating or by crushing. Heating is much more efficient, and it is generally assumed that melting a rock in vacuum will quantitatively degas it after a relatively short time [1].[2] Crushing, however, has a distinct advantage for vesicular samples. Previous work[2-4] has shown that the volatiles in rocks are composed mainly of water and carbon dioxide with smaller amounts of hydrogen, carbon monoxide, methane, nitrogen, and noble gases. The total amount varies widely up to a maximum of over 100 ml standard temperature and pressure (STP)/g. Vacuum extraction with subsequent mass spectrometric analysis of the evolved volatiles was selected as the analytical procedure. The high-vacuum system and experimental procedures are described next.

High-Vacuum System

The high-vacuum gas-handling system (Fig. 1) was constructed of stainless steel and assembled using copper-gasketed Varian ConFlat flanges. The valves were either Varian 3/4 in. all-metal valves or Teflon-sealing Hoke bellows valves. The system was completely free from mercury, grease, or volatile organic materials and was evacuated by a sorption pump and a 30 liter/s Varian Noble VacIon pump. The former proved to be very inconvenient to use, and a rotary-backed diffusion pump was added to the main line so that it could be pumped down independently of the mass spectrometer. The whole of the gas handling system was enclosed in an oven at 120°C to minimize problems due to adsorption of polar compounds, particularly water. This section is shown enclosed by a dashed line in Fig. 1.

---

[2] The italic numbers in brackets refer to the list of references appended to this paper.

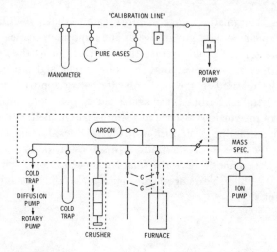

P–Pressure gage.
M–Molecular sieve trap.
C–ConFlat flange.
G–Stainless steel–fused silica graded seal (fused silica tubes)
or mullite-pyrex-stainless steel graded seals (mullite tubes).

FIG. 1–*Schematic diagram of the high-vacuum system. The dashed line encloses all units normally operated at 120°C.*

Furnace

Rock or mineral samples were heated in a fused silica sample tube (5 cm by 0.8 cm diameter) resting inside a larger vertical fused silica or mullite tube. This larger tube was attached to a Varian 1.33-in. ConFlat flange through a graded seal. Fused silica imposes an upper temperature limit of 1200°C, but mullite tubes can be used up to 1700°C. The fused silica tubes were heated by a nichrome-wound resistance furnace. This was controlled by a temperature programmer to give a linear temperature increase of 11°C/min or to hold the temperature at some set value. A 2000°C furnace for use with the mullite tubes is being added to the system.

High-Vacuum Crusher

Samples were crushed in the high-vacuum system using the device shown in Fig. 2. When current was passed through the coils they acted as solenoids and lifted the mild steel weight. Interrupting the current let the weight fall onto the sample[5,6]. By using the coils in different combinations the weight could be dropped from various heights. The available options are listed in Table 1. The sequencing was carried out automatically by a set of motor-driven switches which completed a cycle once every 3 s. The number of drops, which was

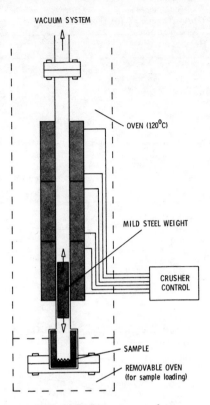

FIG. 2—*High-vacuum crusher.*

displayed on a counter, could be preset with an accuracy of ±1 drop using a built-in timer. In 150 drops the crusher reduced 50 percent of a quarter-gram quartz sample to pass a 200 mesh sieve from starting material of roughly 3-mm cubes. Typical crushing efficiency curves for quartz, fluorite, and basalt are given in Fig. 3. The crusher was mounted inside an oven so that it could be operated at 120°C.

Mass Spectrometer

The volatiles evolved by heating or crushing the rock samples were analyzed with an E.A.I. QUAD 1110 quadrupole mass spectrometer which has a mass range 1 to 300 and unit resolution throughout the range. It includes an electron multiplier as an integral unit, but, since the spectrum was only scanned slowly, the multiplier was bypassed to eliminate drift and improve long term stability. The output was taken from the first dynode and amplified with an Applied Physics Corporation, Model 30M vibrating reed electrometer. The mass spectrometer has an infinitely variable tradeoff between resolution and

TABLE 1—*Options available for the operation of the high vacuum crusher.*

Height of Drop	Sequence
1. Center of coil 1	coil 1, on
	off
2. Center of combined coils 1 and 2	coils 1 and 2, on
	off
3. Center of combined coils 1, 2, and 3	coils 1, 2, and 3, on
	off
4. Center of coil 3 (accelerated down to coil 1, then free fall)	coils 1, 2 and 3, on
	coil 1, off
	coil 2, off
	coil 3, off; coil 1, on
	coil 1, off

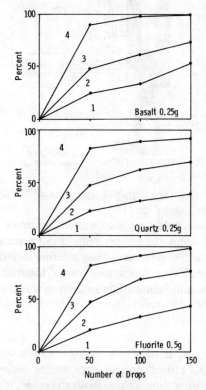

Area 1—passes 200 mesh.
Area 2—60 to 200 mesh.
Area 3—20 to 60 mesh.
Area 4—retained by 20 mesh.

FIG. 3—*Efficiency curves for the high-vacuum crusher. All samples were initially angular pieces with largest dimension about 3 mm.*

sensitivity, and a digital voltmeter was inserted in this circuit so that resolution could be reset precisely. The voltage on the first stage of the electron multiplier could also be displayed on this voltmeter. Temperature has a major effect on instrument stability. The source region was kept at 150°C, and the radio frequency generator at 27°C. Gases were introduced into the mass spectrometer through a Granville-Phillips leak valve.

In order to get accurate gas compositions the mass spectrometer was calibrated, both for the cracking patterns of individual gases and for relative sensitivities. Samples of pure gases were provided in a "calibration line" for this purpose and could be introduced into the mass spectrometer individually or as mixtures of known composition. The mixtures were made by admitting a tap-to-tap volume of the first gas into the calibration line and measuring the pressure, V_1, with the oil manometer. A tap-to-tap volume of the second gas was then added and the new total pressure measured, V_2. The ratio of the components is then $V_1/(V_2 - V_1)$ (since the increase in volume due to the second tap-to-tap volume is negligible). Because the gas analysis is performed in two stages (described next) it was necessary to have values for absolute amounts. A convenient way of achieving this was to add an accurately known quantity of internal standard. Neon was originally used as the standard because of its inertness, low abundance in natural materials and suitable atomic weight. Unfortunately the lighter noble gases are not pumped well by ion pumps and problems with regurgitation and high memory effects were severe. It became necessary to use argon instead since this behaved in a much more satisfactory way. Aliquots of this were taken from a stainless steel reservoir, located in the oven, using a tap-to-tap procedure in the same way that argon-38 aliquots are obtained in potassium-argon dating[7]. Even though the tap-to-tap volume was small compared with the volume of the reservoir the size of the aliquot decreases exponentially as aliquots continue to be withdrawn. In order to define the curve, volumes of the internal standard were calibrated at intervals. These calibrations were carried out using weighed amounts of calcium carbonate which decompose on heating to give accurately known amounts of carbon dioxide. Then, knowing the relative sensitivities for carbon dioxide and argon, the absolute amount of argon follows directly. In practice the relative sensitivity of all the gases were arbitrarily referred to argon = 1. Table 2 summarizes the calibration data used.

Water Determination

With the heated inlet system water could be handled in the same way as other gases and determined mass spectrometrically. Relative sensitivities were found by injecting a known amount of water into the system and measuring the mass spectrometer response compared with a known volume of carbon dioxide obtained by thermally decomposing calcium carbonate. An alternative method

TABLE 2—*Summary of calibration data.*

	Relative Sensitivity (argon = 1.00)	Cracking Pattern
Hydrogen	4.80	
Methane	1.38[a]	14/15 = 0.173; 12/15 = 0.025
Water	2.56	
Carbon monoxide	1.03	12/28 = 0.078
Nitrogen	1.00	14/28 = 0.120
Carbon dioxide	3.57	

[a] Referred to mass 15 peak.

involving dehydration of a weighed amount of barium chloride dihydrate ($BaCl_2 \bullet 2H_2O$) did not give reproducible results.

Analytical Procedure

Extraction of Volatiles

Samples to be crushed were loaded into the bucket at the bottom of the crusher by removing the 2 3/4-in. ConFlat flange. Sample size was normally in the range 0.2 to 0.5 g. For heating, smaller samples of approximately 0.1 g were used. These were weighed into fused silica sample tubes, then put into the larger fused silica or mullite tubes, and reconnected to the high vacuum system via the ConFlat flange. Atmospheric gases were pumped out with the diffusion pump. During the sample heating the trap was kept cool with liquid nitrogen to remove condensable gases (such as water and carbon dioxide) from the hot zone and hence minimize gas-phase reactions.

Adsorption Studies

When rocks and minerals are crushed many new, clean surfaces are generated, and these may adsorb some of the volatiles released by the crushing. This effect has been studied by crushing basalts in the presence of various gases and measuring the reduction in partial pressure using the mass spectrometer. The experimental procedures and results have been described by Barker and Torkelson[8]. They found that water was most strongly absorbed but that adsorption decreased in the order $H_2O>CO_2>CO>CH_4$. Fanale and Cannon[9] have reported similar findings using a different experimental technique. Thus adsorption during gas extraction by crushing changes both the absolute amount of gas and its composition. For lunar basalts Funkhouser et al [10] found that although water (H_2O), carbon monoxide (CO), carbon dioxide (CO_2), and methane (CH_4) are evolved by heating, no water, carbon dioxide, or carbon monoxide was obtained by crushing. Methane, however, was reported in the gases released. It appears that the more strongly adsorbed gases are removed by adsorption on the newly created surfaces. Adsorption of nitrogen and other volatiles on lunar fines have been reported by Grossman et al [11] and Cadenhead et al[12]. Since adsorption is temperature dependent, the amount of gas adsorbed can be reduced by operating the crusher in an oven (see Fig. 2). However, it has been found that at 120°C adsorption is still significant for water and carbon dioxide. It is concluded that crushing may be a useful way of releasing some gases for analysis (such as hydrogen and the noble gases) but that in general it is of no use for quantitative analysis.

Analysis of Volatiles

The volatiles released from heated rocks were separated into two fractions— those that condensed at liquid nitrogen temperatures and those that did not. The condensable volatiles were mainly carbon dioxide and water, and by separating these major components the determination of the minor components was simplified and the accuracy improved. For example, the contribution of carbon dioxide at $m/e = 28$ would account for most of that peak, the balance being nitrogen and carbon monoxide. A small error in the calibration data for the 28/44 ratio for carbon dioxide would have had a very large effect on the apparent contribution of nitrogen and carbon monoxide to the $m/e = 28$ peak and produced large errors in the determination of these gases. There is a second problem in determining trace and major components together because the response of the mass spectrometer is linear only over a limited range. The separation by fractional freezing is shown schematically in Fig. 4. Separate argon internal standards were used for condensable and noncondensable fractions.

The usual procedure involved adding the first argon internal standard during the gas extraction so that efficient mixing with the volatiles occurred. At the end

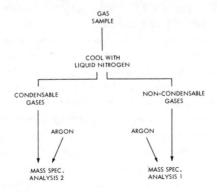

FIG. 4—*Schematic representation of the analytical procedure.*

of the gas extraction either the sample tube or an adjacent tube was cooled with liquid nitrogen for 15 min, and, during this time, the background in the mass spectrometer was scanned and recorded. Then, the mixture of argon and noncondensable gases was introduced into the mass spectrometer by opening the leak valve until the pressure in the mass spectrometer (as registered by the gage on the ion pump) was about 8×10^{-7} torr. The mass spectrum was scanned every 300 s (nominal) and the peak areas measured by the digital integrator. These values, together with the time from the start of the analysis, were printed on a teletype. Four or five scans of the spectrum were normally made, and during this time peak areas fell about 10 percent. When the scans were completed, the gas sample was pumped away, a second argon internal standard introduced into the system, and the liquid nitrogen coolant removed. The condensable gases were left for 1 h to mix with the standard and were then analyzed in the same way as the noncondensables.

Data Handling

The mass spectrometric procedures just outlined generated well over a hundred peaks. Measuring these by hand would be time consuming and introduce the possibility of errors in transcribing data. For these reasons some alternative method of data handling was needed. The system finally selected used a Vidar Autolab 6300T digital integrator to measure peak areas. Although designed to operate with the output from a gas chromatograph, this instrument performed excellently with the output from the vibrating reed electrometer. When used directly with the electron multiplier some preamplification of the signal was necessary. A Speedomax W strip chart recorder was operated in parallel with the digital integrator and gave a permanent record of the analysis. A permanent record of the peak areas was printed by the teletype, each number being identified by the time in seconds from the start of the analysis. The teletype also punched a paper tape which could be subsequently read over a telephone line to the University's Central Computer facility. The data handling system is shown schematically in Fig. 5.

The computer program was written in FORTRAN IV for a Xerox Sigma 6 digital computer. Times and peak areas were read in and separated into individual scans on the basis of time. Since the scan time was 259 s, the program accepted the first peak, at time t, as $m/e = 2$ and then looked at the interval $t + (259 \pm 2)$. A peak in this range with an area within 10 percent of the first mass 2 peak was accepted as the first peak in the second scan. Then using the time for this peak the process could be repeated to identify the first peaks in succeeding scans. Mass-to-charge ratios within each scan were also assigned on the basis of time, since this was related linearly to accelerating voltage, and quadrupole mass spectrometers have a linear relationship between mass-to-charge ratio and accelerating voltage. In the mass spectra of the noncondensable gases there was

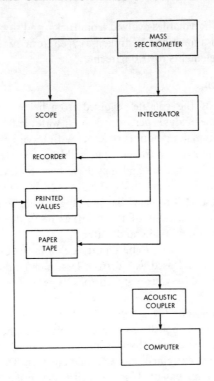

FIG. 5—*Block diagram of the data handling system.*

no (or insignificant) overlap at peaks with m/e = 2, 15, 34, and 40 so that these peaks could be used directly for hydrogen, methane, hydrogen sulfide, and argon, respectively. Oxygen could be determined from the m/e = 32 peak after correcting for any hydrogen sulfide contribution. Nitrogen and carbon monoxide both have parent peaks at m/e = 28 but can be determined separately using the 12 or 14 peaks or both after they have been corrected for any methane contribution. Absolute amounts of the various gases were found by reference to the argon-40 peak, making due allowances for differences in relative sensitivities. The mass spectrum of the condensable gases could be handled in an analogous manner and combined with the composition of the noncondensable gases to give the composition of the total gases evolved from the rock or mineral sample.

Gas compositions expressed in terms of the various chemical compounds probably have little significance since reactions occurring during the high-temperature, low-pressure extraction will radically alter the composition of the volatiles originally present in the rock. For this reason compositions are better expressed in terms of the numbers of atoms of each element if all the reacting species remain in the vapor phase. Carbon, hydrogen, and oxygen account for 95 percent or more of the volatiles evolved from rocks, and so compositions can be conveniently plotted on carbon-hydrogen-oxygen ternary diagrams after normalizing these three elements to 100 percent.

Results and Discussion

Typical analyses of the volatiles evolved from heated terrestrial rocks are given in Table 3. In the analyses performed so far water and carbon dioxide have always been present in major amounts together with lesser amounts of hydrogen, carbon monoxide, methane, nitrogen, and noble gases. Hydrogen sulfide has been absent from all the analyses and may have been removed by reaction with the copper gaskets. Gold plating the gaskets would eliminate this problem. A plot of the data on a C-H-O ternary diagram (Fig. 6) has shown that for all the rocks analyzed the compositions of the volatiles lie in the triangle defined by carbon dioxide, carbon monoxide, and water.

In general, basic rocks appear to be slightly richer in the CO_2-CO component. The amount of volatiles released varied from less than 1 ml(STP)/g to over 100 ml(STP)/g and depended very strongly on rock type with granitic rocks having the most gas.

Triplicate determinations for a basalt sample are given in Table 4 and show excellent agreement for compositions expressed either as individual compounds or as atom percentages of carbon, hydrogen, and oxygen. On the normal ternary diagram the points plot extremely close to one another. The absolute amounts of gas also show good agreement. It is difficult to be certain that the material is the same in all three analyses, since variations between samples of the same rock

TABLE 3—*Typical analyses for the volatiles evolved by heated terrestrial rocks.*

	Percent			
	1	2	3	4
Hydrogen	6.00	3.21	3.23	0.23
Methane	0.00	0.11	0.31	0.11
Water	69.70	63.40	60.00	78.26
Carbon monoxide	1.42	4.64	3.01	2.11
Nitrogen	1.36	3.88	0.35	0.20
Hydrogen sulfide	0.00	0.00	0.00	0.00
Carbon dioxide	21.52	24.76	33.10	19.07
Total (ml/g)	46.06	21.09	36.19	36.84

NOTE—
1 = Granite, pre-Cambrian: Monarch Pass, Colorado. Sintered.
2 = Granite, Mississippian: Rockport, Massachusetts. Sintered.
3 = Basalt, Miocene: Baja, California. Fused.
4 = Basalt, Eocene: S.E. Australia. Fused.

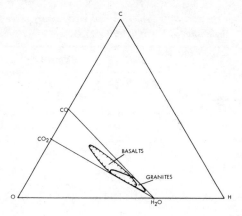

FIG. 6—*Carbon-hydrogen-oxygen ternary diagram (atom percent) showing the fields for basalts (10 samples) and granites (25 samples).*

are potentially large. Differences can be minimized by taking aliquots from one finely crushed sample, although this does increase the amount of adsorbed gas. Other sources of uncertainty are introduced by errors in the volume of the internal standard and in the calibration data. The volume of the internal standard varies very little between successive aliquots so that its effect on the gas composition is negligible, but absolute quantities will be in error by the same percentage as the error in the argon volume. Since the major components (H_2O, CO_2, H_2) are determined from peaks at mass-to-charge ratios which show no overlap with other compounds cracking patterns are of secondary importance in calculating carbon-hydrogen-oxygen percentage. Relative sensitivities are important, however, and introduce errors of approximately ±5 percent.

Most of the gas comes from the rock sample where it may have been present in fluid inclusions, lattice dislocations, structure defects, or as decomposable minerals (for example, hydrates and carbonates). However some of the gas is also adsorbed on surfaces or comes from outgassing of the sample containers. Outgassing can be minimized by a preliminary heating at 1200°C for several days, since blank runs show that on subsequent heating at 1200°C for 3 h the mullite tubes produce 2 to 5 × 10^{-3} ml(STP) of water vapor, together with smaller amounts of nitrogen and carbon monoxide. The quantities are not important for terrestrial samples and can be probably reduced considerably by outgassing the sample tubes at much higher temperatures and by carrying out all sample handling in a nitrogen dry box. The other source of contamination is the gas adsorbed on mineral surfaces. This will be more important for powdered samples than for coarse samples. The quantity of adsorbed gas can be estimated by using the mass spectrometer to monitor the release of volatiles as the

TABLE 4—*Analyses of the volatiles evolved by fusing three separate samples of basalt GA 5316*[18].

	Percent		
	1	2	3
Hydrogen	0.05	0.07	0.06
Methane	0.00	0.00	0.00
Water	93.13	92.95	92.23
Nitrogen	1.53	1.63	1.83
Carbon monoxide	2.14	2.58	2.83
Carbon dioxide	3.16	2.77	3.05
Total gas, ml(STP)/g	17.54	19.20	17.12
Carbon	1.81	1.82	2.02
Hydrogen	63.55	63.61	63.29
Oxygen	34.64	34.56	34.69

temperature is steadily increased up to $1000°C$. Terrestrial rocks generally show a broad, low-temperature peak (100 to $500°C$) which is thought to be produced by the release of the adsorbed volatiles together with those trapped in fluid inclusions. An immediate rerun of the samples shows no low-temperature peak. If the samples are taken out of the vacuum system and exposed to the air overnight monitoring experiments then show that the low-temperature peak has been partially restored. The size of this peak can be used to estimate the amount of adsorbed gas. For coarse terrestrial rocks it is about 2 percent of the total gas released by fusing the rock, but it can reach 10 percent for fine powders.

Lunar rocks are much poorer in volatiles than terrestrial rocks and appear to average about 100 ppm of carbon[13-16] and about 50 ppm of hydrogen [14-16] though much higher values have been reported[17]. These values correspond to 0.2 ml(STP)/g of carbon dioxide and 0.6 ml(STP)/g of hydrogen if these are the only carbon and hydrogen species present. Friedman et al[16] reported 150 to 455 ppm of water in breccias corresponding to 0.2 to 0.6 ml(STP)/g. The methods described can be easily extended to analyze volatiles at these levels. The results given in Table 4 were obtained using 0.1-g samples so that the quantities of carbon dioxide, carbon monoxide, and hydrogen detected were 0.53, 0.44, and 0.011 ml(STP), respectively. Samples with an order of magnitude less gas have been run routinely, and without modification the methods could be used for volatiles at least another order of magnitude less abundant. For 1/2-g samples of lunar basalt this corresponds to limits of detection of approximately 1×10^{-2} ml(STP)/g for carbon monoxide and carbon dioxide, and 5×10^{-4} ml (STP)/g for hydrogen. If the electron multiplier is used, these values can be reduced several orders of magnitude (but with some loss in long term instrument stability). With the present experimental procedures the limits of detection are set not by the analytical system but by the amount of contamination introduced as adsorbed gas or by outgassing of the sample tubes.

Conclusions

The experimental methods developed for quantitatively analyzing the volatiles released from heated rocks have been applied successfully to terrestrial samples. Lunar samples are much poorer in gas, but the analyses reported so far [13-17] show that they fall within the capabilities of the system described.

The composition and abundance of volatiles on the earth and moon have a key role in many theories of lunar origin, since volatiles are particularly sensitive to many physical and chemical processes. It has already been established that lunar rocks are much poorer in volatiles than their terrestrial counterparts and that conditions on the moon were much more reducing. Now it remains to be determined whether there are other significant differences in composition as well. This will involve detailed studies of both terrestrial and lunar samples.

Acknowledgments

We gratefully acknowledge the financial support of the National Aeronautics and Space Administration who through Grant NGR 37-008-002 made this study possible. We would like to thank the many people who supplied samples, and also B. E. Torkelson, J. J. Hayes, and C. C. Dodd for their invaluable assistance.

References

[1] Kirsten, T. in *Potassium Argon Dating*, O. A. Schaeffer and J. Zahringer, Springer Verlag, Berlin, 1966.
[2] Chamberlin, R. T., *The Gases in Rocks*, Cornegie Institute, Washington, 1908.
[3] Shepherd, E. S., *American Journal of Science*, Vol. 35A, 1938, pp. 311-351.
[4] Barker, C. G., *Nature*, Vol. 205, 1965, pp. 1001-1002.
[5] Naughton, J. J., *Nature*, Vol. 197, 1963, pp. 661-663.
[6] Barker, C. G., "The Quantitative Determination of Some Volatile Constituents Evolved by Rocks and Minerals on Heating," D. Phil. thesis, Oxford University, Oxford, England, 1965.
[7] Lanphere, M. A. and Dalrymple, G. B., *Nature*, Vol. 209, 1966, pp. 902-903.
[8] Barker, C. G. and Torkelson, B. E., "Gas Adsorption on Crushed Quartz and Basalt," submitted to *Nature*, 1973.
[9] Fanale, F. P. and Cannon, W. A., *Nature*, Vol. 230, 1971, pp. 502-504.
[10] Funkhouser, J., Jessberger, E., Muller, O., and Zahringer, J., *Proceedings*, Second Lunar Science Conference, *Geochimica et Cosmochimica Acta*, Supplement 2, The MIT Press, Cambridge, Mass., 1971, p. 1388.
[11] Grossman, J. J., Mukherjee, N. R., and Ryan, J. A., *Proceedings*, Third Lunar Science Conference, *Geochimica et Cosmochimica Acta*, Supplement 3, The MIT Press, Cambridge, Mass., 1972, pp. 2259-2269.
[12] Cadenhead, D. A., Wagner, N. J., Jones, B. R., and Stetter, J. R., *Proceedings*, Third Lunar Science Conference, *Geochimica et Cosmochimica Acta*, Supplement 3, The MIT Press, Cambridge, Mass., 1972, pp. 2243-2257.

[13] Chang, S. and Kvenvolden, K. A. in *Exobiology,* C. Ponnamperuma, ed., North Holland, Amsterdam, 1971, Chapter 12.

[14] Epstein, S. and Taylor, H. P., Jr., *Proceedings,* Second Lunar Science Conference, *Geochimica et Cosmochimica Acta,* Supplement 2, The MIT Press, Cambridge, Mass., 1971, p. 1427.

[15] Friedman, I., O'Neil, J. R., Gleason, J. D., and Hardcastle, K., *Proceedings,* Second Lunar Science Conference, *Geochimica et Cosmochimica Acta,* Supplement 2, The MIT Press, Cambridge, Mass., 1971, p. 1412.

[16] Friedman, I., Gleason, J. D., and Hardcastle, K. G., *Proceedings,* Apollo 11 Lunar Science Conference, *Geochimica et Cosmochimica Acta,* Supplement 1, Pergamon, New York, 1970, pp. 1103-1109.

[17] Hintenberger, H., Weber, H. W., Voshage, H., Wanke, H. Begemann, F., Vilscek, E., and Wlotzka, F., *Science,* Vol. 167, 1970, pp. 543-545.

[18] Webb, A. W., Stevens, N. C., and McDougall, I., *Proceedings,* Royal Society of Queensland, Vol. 79, 1967, pp. 79-92.

D. J. DesMarais,[1] J. M. Hayes,[1] and W. G. Meinschein[1]

Techniques for the Analysis of Gases Sequentially Released from Lunar Samples

REFERENCE: DesMarais, D. J., Hayes, J. M., and Meinschein, W. G., "Techniques for the Analysis of Gases Sequentially Released from Lunar Samples," *Analytical Methods Developed for Application to Lunar Samples Analyses, ASTM STP 539*, American Society for Testing and Materials, 1973, pp. 71–79.

ABSTRACT: This paper describes two methods for the analysis of light gases that are sequentially evolved from 2 to 10 mg of lunar sample. A hydrofluoric acid hydrolysis of lunar material is achieved by repeated exposure of the sample to hydrogen fluoride. In the second technique, gases are evolved from lunar samples by the stepwise heating of these samples to 1400°C. The gases evolved by either hydrolysis or pyrolysis are analyzed in a gas chromatographic system using a helium ionization detector. The sensitivities of this detector for the gases, as analyzed, range from 2×10^{-11} g/s for hydrogen to 2×10^{-13} g/s for carbon dioxide.

KEY WORDS: lunar analysis, pyrolysis, gas chromatography, carbon, helium, gas analysis, acid hydrolysis

Considerable effort has been expended to characterize the occurrence of carbon in lunar samples. Many of the procedures used in the study of Apollo 11 samples were designed to detect high molecular weight carbon compounds of possible biogenic origin[1-3].[2] The results obtained by such procedures are principally negative, but investigations employing gas chromatographic analysis of aqueous hydrofluoric acid (HF) hydrolysis and pyrolysis products have established that the bulk of lunar carbon can be released as low molecular weight gases [4-6]. Various aqueous acids and isotopically labelled reagents have provided additional definition of the distributions and possible compositions of carbon species in Apollo 12 samples [7-9]. Results on pyrolysis products have indicated that the preponderance of lunar carbon is evolved as carbon monoxide

---

[1] Research assistant, Department of geology, assistant professor of chemistry and geology, Department of Chemistry, and professor of geology, Department of geology respectively, Indiana University, Bloomington, Ind. 47401.

[2] The italic numbers in brackets refer to the list of references appended to this paper.

(CO), carbon dioxide (CO_2), and methane (CH_4) [4-6,10,11]. These pyrolysis experiments generally have required samples weighing in excess of 100 mg per analysis. This paper presents a method for the gradational etching of lunar samples using gaseous HF or deuterium fluoride (DF) and a sensitive pyrolysis method requiring 10 mg or less of lunar materials per analysis. These analytical techniques make it feasible to investigate the distributions of carbon compounds in the various size fractions and monomineralic components of lunar samples.

Equipment

Analytical System

All tubing and Swagelok fittings of the system (Fig. 1) are constructed of stainless steel. The fittings and tubing were extracted sequentially with distilled water, methanol, and chloroform prior to assembly, and the tubing was heated to a red glow and purged with helium.

Carrier Gas

Matheson UHP Grade helium is employed as carrier gas. The helium tank is fitted with an all-metal gas regulator (Tescom Corp.). The helium gas is filtered through a liquid nitrogen cooled trap into the analytical system. This trap consists of a 6.2 mm inside diameter by 120 cm length coiled stainless steel tube, packed with 100 to 120 mesh size 5 Å molecular sieve (Linde).

Detector Calibration

A measured quantity of reference gas mixture is injected into the exponential dilution flask [12]. Carrier gas flow into this flask is regulated by a flow controller (Veriflow Corp.), and the helium flow exponentially dilutes the reference gases. Aliquots of the diluted reference gases from the flask are

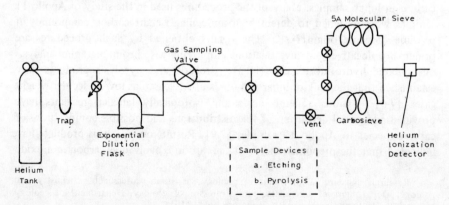

FIG. 1—*Overall gas analysis system.*

injected into the analytical system by means of a eight-port helium jacketed sampling valve (Valco Inc.). The helium jacket prevents measurable leakages of atmospheric gases into the system if the helium flow through the jacket exceeds 8 ml/min. Calibrations for the individual reference gases are recorded as plots of concentrations versus gas chromatographic peak areas.

Sample Valves

A metal valving system (Fig. 1) permits the helium flow to be directed either through the etching or pyrolysis device or directly into the gas chromatograph. The vent valve provides a direct exhaust for atmospheric gases after a sample cell has been opened.

Chromatographic Instrument

The gas chromatograph (Varian Model 1532) is modified to accept two Pyrex glass columns, 2 mm inside diameter by 4 m in length, each utilizing the same helium ionization detector. Metal valves are used to direct helium flow through either of the columns and the detector. The columns are packed with 100 to 120 mesh size substrates. One column contains carbon molecular sieve (Supelco Co. "Carbosieve B"), and the other column contains 5 Å molecular sieve. Analyses have shown that these substrates are acceptable column packings for the separation of gases evolved from lunar samples [13-14]. In this laboratory, the carbon molecular sieve column resolves hydrogen (H_2), nitrogen (N_2), CH_4, CO, and CO_2 in approximately 20 min at 50°C with a 40 ml/min carrier gas flow. A carrier gas back pressure of approximately 30 psig is required to maintain this flow. Previous investigations demonstrate that a 5 Å molecular sieve column resolves H_2, argon, and oxygen at subambient temperatures [14].

Helium Ionization Detector

The helium ionization detector (Varian Inc.)[15], is sensitive to all light gases except helium. Practical detection limits (3/1 signal to noise ratio) for this detector at an operating potential of 360 V using a carbon molecular sieve column are in flow rates of grams per second as follows: $H_2 = 2 \times 10^{-11}$, $N_2 = 3 \times 10^{-12}$, $CH_4 = 5 \times 10^{-13}$, $CO = 1 \times 10^{-12}$, and $CO_2 = 2 \times 10^{-13}$. The great sensitivity of the detector necessitates maintaining the atmospheric leakage into the system below 10^{-12} g/s. Also, trace impurities in the helium gas cause detector background levels to attain a high value at temperatures above 100°C, and this system becomes unusable at full detector voltage or maximum sensitivity at such temperatures. The low internal volume of the helium ionization detector makes it compatible with the collection of individual gas fractions—a procedure to be utilized in carbon isotopic measurements.

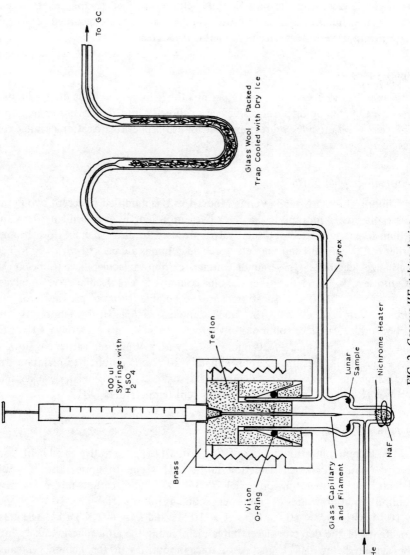

FIG. 2.–*Gaseous HF etching device.*

Acid Etching System

Pure gaseous HF is produced in the system (Fig. 2) by reactions of reagent grade sulfuric acid metered from a syringe onto sodium fluoride (NaF). Before use, the NaF is dissolved in a 40 percent HF solution and evaporated to dryness to remove traces of CO_2. This etching system makes it possible to etch lunar material by repeated doses of HF (or DF) gas. Because the diffusion rate of HF in the gas phase is approximately 10^5 greater than HF in the aqueous phase, the gaseous HF facilitates a uniform etching of the sample surface, and repeated treatments with HF gas permits the etching to occur at gradually increasing depths below this surface. Figure 3 presents a graph of the amounts of H_2 released by sequential gaseous HF treatments of Apollo 14 lunar fines.

The etching system (Fig. 2) is designed to eliminate direct access of metal parts to HF. The Pyrex reaction vessel is sealed from the brass clamping device by a Teflon cap and compression seal containing a Viton O-ring. These fluorocarbon caps and seals produce negligible amounts of interfering gases in the presence of HF and effectively seal the reaction vessel at pressures up to 50 psig.

Pyrolysis System

Stainless steel and nickel sample cells release carbon gases at elevated temperatures and are unacceptable for pyrolysis analysis runs at the sensitivity levels used in this investigation. Quartz tubes (Fig. 4), baked at 1250°C for at least 18 h with a helium purge, are satisfactory as pyrolysis cells and permit measurement of gases to the levels reported in Fig. 5. The heating element is 20 gage furnace grade platinum wire wrapped around an aluminum oxide tube, coated with aluminum oxide cement, and enclosed in firebrick. A platinum-

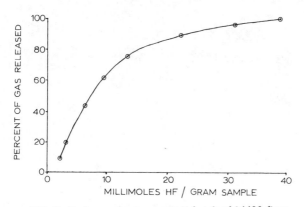

FIG. 3—*Hydrogen from a sequential etch of 14422 fines.*

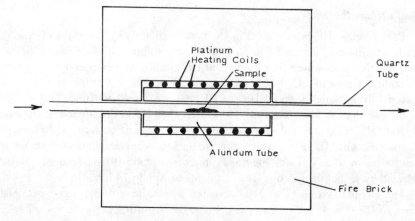

FIG. 4—*Pyrolysis oven.*

platinum 13 percent rhodium thermocouple within the aluminum oxide tube is used to monitor the oven temperature.

Sample Handling and Analytical Procedures

Glassware

Prior to use, all glassware used in handling lunar material is acid cleaned in 1:1 volume/volume concentrated sulfuric acid (H_2SO_4) and nitric acid for several hours at $110°C$, rinsed in distilled water followed by purified methanol, and dried in an oven at $110°C$. The quartz pyrolysis cell, as described above, is cleaned only by heating and purging with helium.

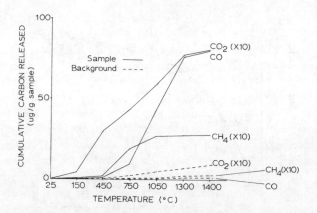

FIG. 5—*Pyrolysis of 15100,9 fines (8.5-mg sample).*

Sample Handling

A portion of lunar sample is transferred from its shipping container to a small (6 mm by 1 cm) Pyrex boat by means of a glass spatula and weighed. The sample in the boat is retained in a weighing bottle with a hand ground 45/12 standard taper glass cap until the sample is transferred to the etching or pyrolysis cell. The sample boat is reweighed to determine the amount of sample transferred.

Gas Injection into Chromatograph

Gas injection is accomplished by manipulation of the two valves, center and left of center, above the sample devices (Fig. 1). The valve to left of center, above the sample, is opened first, then the center or bypassing valve is closed. After the helium flow sweeps the sample device for 15 s, the bypassing valve is again opened, and the sample valve is closed. Carefully executed valve operation is required to minimize carrier gas flow perturbations, a source of "ghost" peaks, and to ensure reproducible injections as well as sharp chromatogaphic peaks.

Acid Etching

After the lunar sample and NaF are placed into the chamber, as indicated in Fig. 2, and the chamber is sealed, the device is baked at $70°C$ for a few hours with a helium purge. The trap (Fig. 2) is then cooled in a dry ice-methanol bath, and the NaF is heated to $200°C$ by an encircling heater coil. H_2SO_4 (D_2SO_4) is dripped from the syringe onto the NaF, one to two microliters per addition. The evolved HF (DF) etches the surfaces of the lunar sample, releasing entrapped gases and forming gaseous products. After a 15 to 20 min reaction period, the gases are swept by helium from the chamber through the cold trap and into the chromatographic column. The cold trap removes most of the unreacted HF (DF) and the water, formed as a reaction product, from the gases that are to be analyzed. The total H_2SO_4 used in several sequential additions during a sample analysis is limited to approximately 10 μl because the sodium sulfate reaction product then covers the remaining NaF and retards further HF production. Assuming quantitative release and reaction of HF, 10 μl of H_2SO_4 will cause 2.8 mg of silica to be etched. Although some of the evolved HF reacts with the Pyrex chamber, sufficient gases are released from a few milligrams of lunar materials by the preceding method to provide definitive results. Figure 3 shows that most of the hydrogen in a lunar soil is released by the initial etching. This illustrates that most of the hydrogen is located on the surfaces of the soil particles.

Pyrolysis

Lunar sample is inserted in the 6-mm outside diameter quartz sample tube with a narrow glass spatula. The tube is inserted into the oven (Fig. 4), and its ends attached to the two sample leads (Fig. 1).

Helium flow bypasses the tube while the sample is kept within a selected temperature range for a measured period of time. At the outset of an experiment, gas is collected with the oven temperature at 150°C. Gases evolved at this temperature are presumed to be contamination. After gas evolution at 150°C ceases, the temperature of tube is increased at the rate 10°C/ min. Injections into the gas chromatograph are made at 30 min intervals, thus allowing the most abundant carbon gases to elute from the carbon molecular sieve column before the next injection is made. The results of such a sample analysis are shown in Fig. 5.

Acknowledgment

This work has been supported by NASA Grant NGR 15-003-105, and certain laboratory facilities utilized for this investigation were supplied by NSF Grants 6583, and 14687.

References

[1] Kvenvolden, K. A., Chang, S., Smith, J. W., Flores, J., Pering, K., Saxinger, D., Woeller, F., Kiel, K., Berger, I., and Ponnamperuma, C., *Proceedings,* Apollo 11 Lunar Science Conference, *Geochimica et Cosmochimica Acta,* Vol. 2, Pergamon, New York, Jan. 1970, pp. 1813-1328.

[2] Meinschein, W. G., Jackson, T. J., Mitchell, J. M., Cordes, E., and Shiner, V. J., *Proceedings,* Apollo 11 Lunar Science Conference, *Geochimica et Cosmochimica Acta,* Vol. 2, Pergamon, New York, Jan. 1970, pp. 1875-1877.

[3] Rho, J. H., Bauman, A. J., Yen, T. F., and Bonner, J., *Proceedings,* Apollo 11 Lunar Science Conference, *Geochimica et Cosmochimica Acta,* Vol. 2, Pergamon, New York, Jan. 1970, pp. 1929-1932.

[4] Abell, P. I., Draffan, C. H., Eglinton, G., Hayes, J. M., Maxwell, J. R., and Pillinger, C. T., *Proceedings,* Apollo 11 Lunar Science Conference, *Geochimica et Cosmochimica Acta,* Vol. 2, Pergamon, New York, Jan. 1970, pp. 1757-1773.

[5] Chang, S., Smith, J. W., Kaplan, I., Lawless, J., Kvenvolden, K. A., and Ponnamperuma, C., *Proceedings,* Apollo 11 Lunar Science Conference, *Geochimica et Cosmochimica Acta,* Vol. 2, Pergamon, New York, Jan. 1970, pp. 1857-1869.

[6] Oro, J., Updegrove, W. S., Gibert, J., McReynolds, J., Gil-Av, E., Ibanez, J., and Zlatkis, A., *Proceedings,* Apollo 11 Lunar Science Conference, *Geochimica et Cosmochimica Acta,* Vol. 2, Pergamon, New York, Jan. 1970, pp. 1901-1920.

[7] Abell, P. I., Cadogan, P. H., Eglinton, G., Maxwell, J. R., and Pillinger, C. T., *Proceedings,* Second Lunar Science Conference, *Geochimica et Cosmochimica Acta,* Vol. 2, The MIT Press, Cambridge, Mass., Jan. 1971, pp. 1843-1863.

[8] Cadogan, P. H., Eglinton, G., Maxwell, J. R., and Pillinger, C. T., *Nature,* Vol. 231, May 1971, pp. 29-31.

[9] Oro, J., Flory, D. A., McReynolds, J., Gibert, J. M., Lichtenstein, H. A., and Wikstrom, S., *Proceedings,* Second Lunar Science Conference, *Geochimica et Cosmochimica Acta,* Vol. 2, The MIT Press, Cambridge, Mass., Jan. 1971, pp. 1913-1925.

[10] Burlingame, A. L., Calvin, M., Han, J., Henderson, W., Reed, W., and Simoneit, B. R., *Proceedings,* Apollo 11 Lunar Science Conference, *Geochimica et Cosmochimica Acta,* Vol. 2, Pergamon, New York, Jan. 1970, pp. 1779-1791.
[11] Moore, C. B., Gibson, E. K., Larimer, J. W., Lewis, C. F., Nichiporuk, W., *Proceedings,* Apollo 11 Lunar Science Conference, *Geochimica et Cosmochimica Acta,* Vol. 2, Pergamon, New York, Jan. 1970, pp. 1375-1382.
[12] Lovelock, J. E. in *Gas Chromatography 1960,* R. P. W. Scott, ed., Butterworth, London, 1960, p. 26.
[13] Zlatkis, A., Kaufman, H. R., and Darbin, D. E., *Journal of Chromatographic Science,* Vol. 8, No. 7, July 1970, pp. 416-417.
[14] Gunther, B. D. and Musgrave, B. C., *Journal of Gas Chromatography,* Vol. 4, No. 4, April 1966, p. 162.
[15] Hartmann, C. H. and Dimick, K. P., *Journal of Gas Chromatography,* Vol. 4, No. 5, May 1966, pp. 163-167.

P. A. Estep,[1] *J. J. Kovach,*[1] *and C. Karr*[1]

Microsampling Techniques for Infrared Spectroscopic Analysis of Lunar and Terrestrial Minerals

REFERENCE: Estep, P. A., Kovach, J. J., and Karr, C., Jr., "Microsampling Techniques for Infrared Spectroscopic Analysis of Lunar and Terrestrial Minerals," *Analytical Methods Developed for Application to Lunar Samples Analyses, ASTM STP 539,* American Society for Testing and Materials, 1973, pp. 80–99.

ABSTRACT: Microsampling techniques have been developed for infrared analysis of single mineral grains (>150 μm) from lunar rocks and dusts, allowing a detailed molecular structure characterization of these complex fine-grained samples. The methods include special devices for isolating single grains, preparing micropellets from the grains, and obtaining *in situ* microspecular reflectance spectra from grains in polished rock samples. Although specifically developed for the work on lunar samples, the special techniques for single grain infrared analysis were found to be equally useful in studies of complex terrestrial mineral samples. For example, infrared microanalysis has contributed substantially in solving problems concerned with our natural resources, such as the structural characterization of minerals from commercial iron ores, marine deposits, coal, and fly ash derived from coal.

KEY WORDS: infrared spectroscopy, lunar analysis, infrared reflectance, iron ores, coal minerals, fly ash, marine deposits, lunar mineralogy, microanalysis, lunar dust

In molecular structure characterization studies of minerals from lunar samples by infrared absorption spectroscopy, we were required to obtain spectra on isolated single grains (150 to 1000 μm) and on grains *in situ* in polished rock samples[1,2].[2] The grain isolations and stringent sample handling requirements necessitated the development of some unique microsampling devices and procedures that are not commercially available or described in the literature as standard techniques for infrared spectroscopy. The application of single grain

---

[1] Research chemists, U.S. Bureau of Mines, Morgantown Energy Research Center, Morgantown, W. Va. 26505.

[2] The italic numbers in brackets refer to the list of references appended to this paper.

infrared analysis to fine-grained composite lunar samples has enabled us to obtain spectra of minerals in a very pure state, to detect grain-to-grain structural variations within mineral classes, to identify trace accessory minerals, and to obtain infrared, Raman, and optical spectra on the same single grain.

Although specifically designed for the work on lunar samples, we found that the special techniques and their advantages could be applied equally well in the spectroscopic analysis of terrestrial rocks and minerals. Therefore, this paper will describe both our application of the microsampling techniques to the analysis of lunar rocks and dusts and their application in solving problems concerned with uses of terrestrial natural resources—such as the characterization of minerals in commercial iron ores, in marine deposits, and in coal and coal-derived products.

Lunar Sample Studies

Isolation of Grains from Lunar Samples

Lunar samples were received as 1 to 2 g of dusts (<1 mm fines) and 1 to 3 g of rock chips; all sampling from these were conducted in a nitrogen-purged dry box. Sized grains from the dusts and crushed rock chips were obtained by dry sieving. For separating these small quantities, we used the sieving vial shown in Fig. 1, which gave better quantitative recovery of total material than could be obtained with larger commercially available microsieves. The vial ("Opticlear," Wards Natural Science Establishment, Inc., Rochester, N.Y.[3]) is fitted with a polyethylene cap that has a snap-out lid. The bottom of the cap was cut out, and, as shown in the assembled view of Fig. 1, a piece of 100 mesh nylon screen (Nitex," nylon monofilament screen cloth, meeting ASTM specification E 11-58T for size and uniformity of mesh; Tobler, Ernst, and Traber, Inc., New York, N.Y.) was inserted between the cap and vial. The sample was placed on top of the screen, and, with the lid of the cap snapped into place, vigorous shaking could be carried out with security. For good sieving efficiency, no more than 500 mg of sample should be sieved at one time in the 3-dram vial. Larger amounts can be obtained in a single sieving by using a 5-dram vial. Screens with openings larger than a size of 80 mesh were found to be too inflexible to be used in these small vials. Although sieved fractions from + 100 to +400 mesh (yielding grains as small as 37 μm) were separated in this work, it was feasible to isolate individual grains microscopically for infrared analysis only from the +100 mesh fraction (>150 μm).

The +100 mesh sample was placed in the center area of a specially designed glass sorting stage, shown in Fig. 2. Individual grains were sorted and classified on this stage under low-power magnification ($\times$10 to 60) using a binocular microscope on which were mounted two alpha-emitters to neutralize electro-

[3] Equipment is named in the report for identification only and does not necessarily imply endorsement by the U.S. Bureau of Mines.

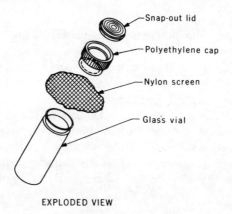

Snap-out lid
Polyethylene cap
Nylon screen
Glass vial

EXPLODED VIEW

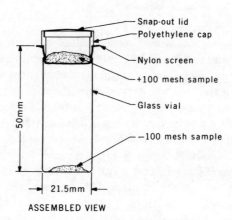

Snap-out lid
Polyethylene cap
Nylon screen
+100 mesh sample
Glass vial
—100 mesh sample

50mm

21.5mm

ASSEMBLED VIEW

FIG. 1—*Three-dram sieving vial.*

static charges ("Staticmaster," 500 μ-Curies, Nuclear Products Co., El Monte, Calif.). Individual grains were photographed on the center section of this stage, as shown for example in Fig. 3 for fragments chipped from lunar rock 12021,24. Photomacrographic techniques were used and the magnification most suitable for closeups of grains isolated from the +100 mesh sieved fractions (150 to 1000 μm) was obtained with an extension of 300 mm between a 35-mm camera body and a 28-mm-wide angle lens (reverse mounted), giving a 3-mm field-of-view. After photography, sorted grains were stored in the individual wells of the stage shown in Fig. 2, and more sample (not over 200 mg) was added to the center section of the stage for continued sorting. To recover a grain from a storage well, a fine-tipped probe fabricated from flattened copper wire was used to move the

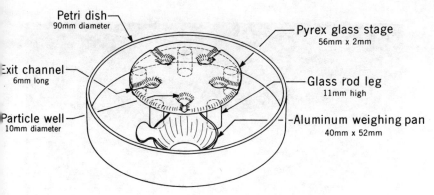

FIG. 2–*Glass stage for microscopic sorting of mineral grains.*

grain down the exit channel and over the rounded edge into a small aluminum weighing pan. It was necessary that all edges of the well and exit channel be well rounded and smooth surfaced for maximum control of the probe and grain movement. A well-rounded rim on the glass stage also allowed direct recovery from the stage if well storage was not desired. As seen in Fig. 2, both the footed glass stage and weighing pan were placed in a Petri dish to allow recovery of any spilled material and to facilitate positioning of the stage under the microscope. Recovered grains were weighed in the recovery pan on a microbalance.

Preparation of Single Grains for Infrared Spectroscopy

In the first application of infrared absorption spectroscopy to the analysis of lunar samples[3] we utilized macrosampling methods which require about 1000 μg of sample to produce a suitable infrared spectrum. This amount of sample was blended with 500 mg of cesium iodide matrix to form a 13-mm-diameter by 0.8-mm-thick pellet. Since single lunar grains that could be feasibly isolated (150 to 1000 μm) were in the weight range of 20 to 900 μg (typically 100 μg) it was necessary to combine several grains of one kind to obtain the 1000 μg required for macroanalysis. For example, all of the 349 ilmenite grains (averaging 100 μm) shown sorted in Fig. 3 were required to prepare an infrared macropellet. These grain combinations presented several disadvantages. Any grain-to-grain structural variations within a mineral class could not be detected, cross-contamination of minerals was possible during the selections, trace accessory minerals could not be studied, and other data such as Raman and optical spectra could not be obtained on the same sample examined for the infrared analysis. These disadvantages were removed by using infrared microsampling techniques in which an infrared spectrum could be obtained on a single grain as small as 150 μm, as shown for example by some of the ilmenite grains in Fig. 3. After a grain was selected, recovered from the sorting stage, and weighed, optical and Raman

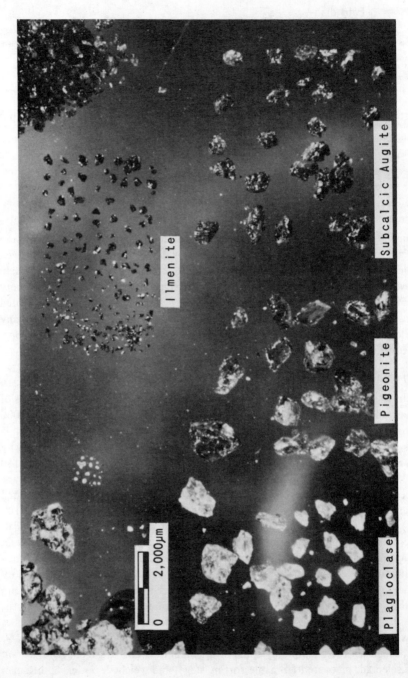

FIG. 3—Sorted mineral grains from lunar crystalline basalt 12021 24

spectra [1] were obtained on the grain prior to infrared analysis. To obtain a Raman spectrum or to carry out thermal studies, the grain was placed in a 0.5-mm-diameter fused-quartz capillary (commonly used for X-ray diffraction powder camera work; Uni-Mex Co., Griffith, Ind.) utilizing a hand-blown glass microfunnel with a 15-mm-diameter top. The thin-walled capillary (10 μm) could be sealed easily under inert atmosphere and gave no interfering lines when Raman spectra were taken. The capillaries were also refractory enough to allow heating to 1000°C in thermal studies that we made on single grains.

After all other data were obtained, a grain was recovered and ground in air to a fine powder for infrared microsampling analysis, utilizing a specially designed microcrushing mortar similar to the macrocrushing mortar previously described [3]. The crushing mortar, shown in Fig. 4, consists of a 25 mm inside diameter mullite mortar fitted with a specially designed stainless steel funneled-cylinder. A retaining plate secured by two wing nuts was used to fit the cylinder tightly in the mortar, as shown in the sectional view. A stainless steel plunger was tapped lightly down through the cylinder opening onto a confined grain, producing completely recoverable crushed fragments on the mortar surface. It was essential to confine in this manner the small glass beads isolated from the lunar dusts, since these could be lost easily because of static charges. The cylinder assembly was removed, and the crushed fragments were hand ground, without transfer, using the conventional pestle for this mortar. Since the grain was so small, only a few taps of the plunger and subsequent limited grinding were required to reduce the size of the grain below that necessary for maximum absorption and

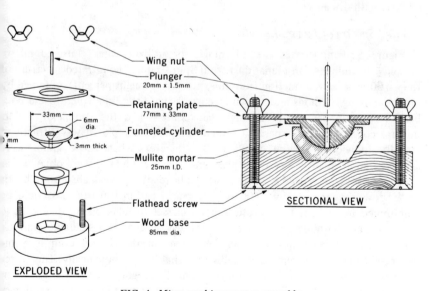

FIG. 4—*Microcrushing mortar assembly.*

minimum reflection of infrared radiation. Excessive grinding was found to deteriorate mineral structure and produce poor quality spectra.

Cesium iodide was next added to produce a mixture with a sample concentration of approximately 0.3 weight percent. For grains ranging in size from 150 to 1000 μm and weighing 20 to 900 μg, the amount of cesium iodide required ranged from 6 to 270 mg. Less than 6 mg of powder presented difficulties in forming a recoverable micropellet. The mixture was blended and then transferred to an ultramicro die (Perkin-Elmer Corp., Norwalk, Conn.). A micropellet was pressed in the 1.5 mm center opening of a 13-mm-diameter by 1-mm-thick steel sample disk under vacuum at 500 lb total load. The micropellet, still mounted in the sample disk, was then placed in a reflecting-type X6 ultramicro beam condenser (Perkin-Elmer Corp.), mounted on a Model 621 Perkin-Elmer grating infrared spectrophotometer that was purged with dry air. The beam condenser, consisting of two ellipsoidal condensing mirrors and two flat mirrors to divert the beam through the sample and back into the monochromator, reduced the transmission to about 30 percent at 4000 cm^{-1}. To restore transmission to 80 percent, the reference beam was attenuated. Sufficient energy was still available to give acceptable photometric accuracy and to produce an infrared spectrum with band resolution comparable to that obtained under normal scanning conditions. Absorption bands of atmospheric water vapor and carbon dioxide, produced by the increased path length in the sample beam with use of this accessory, were removed from the spectrum by purging both the sample and reference beam compartments of the spectrophotometer with dry air.

Infrared Spectra of Lunar Minerals

Figure 5 demonstrates the advantages of utilizing these infrared micro-sampling techniques for a lunar dust from Spur Crater. The infrared spectrum of the −100 mesh sieved fraction from this dust (84.5 weight percent), obtained by macrosampling methods and shown as curve a, has little fine structure and poor band resolution because of its high-glass content and the complexity of its mineral composition. In spectra of such composite samples it was difficult to identify individual mineral constituents. However, when single grains were sampled, good quality spectra of glass and specific minerals were obtained, as seen in curves b, c, d, and e. From positions of relatively weak absorption bands in the low-frequency region (400 to 200 cm^{-1}) cation substitutions could be determined in each of the silicate mineral classes of feldspars, pyroxenes, and olivines[1,3]. Within single lunar samples we observed considerable grain-to-grain structural variations for each of these silicate classes, even in some instances when grains were nearly indistinguishable morphologically. The degree of sample inhomogeneity determined from these grain structural variation could be then applied in deducing genetic histories of the samples, a primary

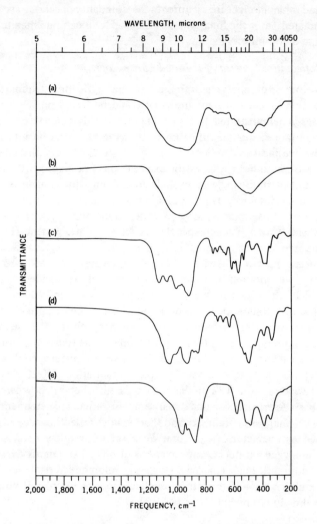

FIG. 5—*Infrared spectra of mineral grains from lunar dust 15301, 83 from Spur Crater:*
(a) −100 mesh sieved fraction, representative sample; (b) glass, 200 × 200 μm light green
transparent fragment; (c) plagioclase, 200 × 200 μm colorless transparent grain; (d)
pyroxene, 300 × 300 μm light yellow transparent grain; (e) olivine, 400 × 300 μm golden
yellow transparent grain.

goal of lunar sample analyses. The use of single grain analysis also enabled us to identify and characterize the structures of some minor and trace accessory minerals isolated from the lunar samples, such as for example ilmenite, α-quartz, ülvospinel, and chromite.

Infrared Reflectance Spectra of Polished Lunar Rock Samples

The feasibility of applying infrared specular reflection techniques to the characterization of mineral structures that could be found on the lunar surface was previously demonstrated by Lyon [4]. Using this nondestructive sampling method to obtain *in situ* identifications and crystal orientation information for single grains, we measured reflectance spectra directly from polished samples of lunar rocks. Some lunar rocks, as for example the Fra Mauro breccia shown in Fig. 6, contained pure single grain inclusions from which infrared reflectance spectra could be obtained. The complex rock-type shown in Fig. 6 is believed to have been formed by impact processes which cemented together both dust and rock fragments. With a microspecular reflectance attachment (Perkin-Elmer Corp.) mounted on the infrared instrument, and utilizing masks with 1 and 2-mm-diameter apertures (with effective apertures of 0.5 and 1.5 mm, respectively), we obtained near-normal (13-deg angle of incidence) reflectance spectra which allowed structural characterizations of embedded grains. For example, the reflectance spectrum of a yellow grain (pictured at the lower right in Fig. 6) is shown in Fig. 7 (curve *c*) to match favorably with those of synthetic samples of a clinohypersthene (curve *a*) and a pigeonite (curve *b*), indicating that the grain is a calcium-poor, iron-rich clinopyroxene. For terrestrial standards, in order to eliminate unique crystallographic orientation effects, we obtained reflectance spectra from 13-mm-diameter pressed pellets of powdered samples. Lyon [5] has shown that for powdered samples, reflectance frequencies remain constant with changes in grain size and that powder reflection spectra, therefore, can be used to characterize structure. We observed frequency shifts in powder spectra of analyzed plagioclase, pyroxene, and olivine standards that correlated well with compositional changes. However, reference reflectance spectra of oriented single crystals of terrestrial standards are needed to fully interpret the lunar data already obtained by this technique.

Application of Microsampling Techniques in Terrestrial Mineral Analyses

Minerals from Commercial Iron Ore

The Bureau of Mines is studying methods for beneficiation of commercial low-grade iron ores for optimum utilization by industry. To aid in the development of these processes, we have applied infrared microanalysis to a determination of the mineralogy of natural ores and to the detection of some specific structural changes that occur in iron minerals during roasting for

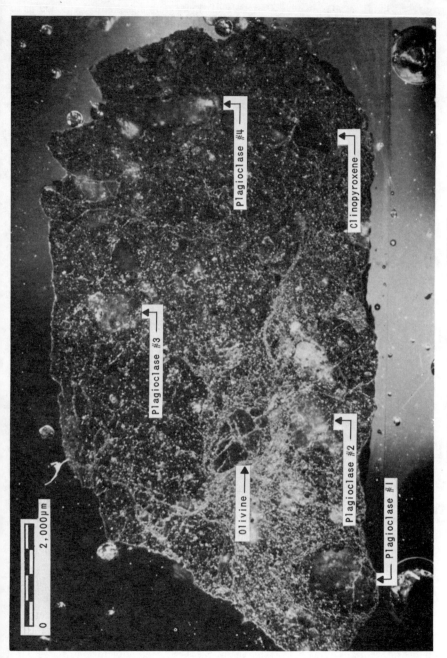

FIG. 6—Polished sample of lunar breccia 14321, 97.

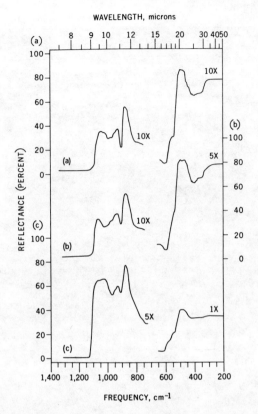

FIG. 7–*Infrared reflection spectra, 2 mm mask:* (a) *clinohypersthene* (En_{50} Fs_{50}), *synthetic pressed powder (Tem-Pres Research Division, The Carborundum Co., State College, Pa.)*; (b) *pigeonite* ($Wo_{10}Fs_{45}En_{45}$), *synthetic pressed powder (Tem-Pres)*; (c) *clinopyroxene, 600 × 600 μm yellow transparent grain in lunar polished butt 14321, 97.*

beneficiation. Figure 8 shows typical grains isolated from the +100 mesh sieved fraction of a sample of natural taconite ore from Minnesota. Petrographic modal analysis showed that the ore sample consisted of 44 percent quartz, 41 percent hematite, and 10 percent hydrated iron oxides. The infrared spectrum of a representative sample of this composition obtained by macrosampling methods is shown as curve *a* in Fig. 9. Absorption bands of quartz dominate the spectrum because of their high infrared absorptivities, making it difficult to detect absorption bands of the iron minerals. However, by making single grain isolations from the ore sample we were able to obtain well-resolved spectra of hematite (α-ferric oxide (Fe_2O_3)), as shown for example in curve *b*, Fig. 9. This spectrum, excluding some weak bands of quartz, matched well with those of samples of the kidney ore variety of hematite. When the ore sample was

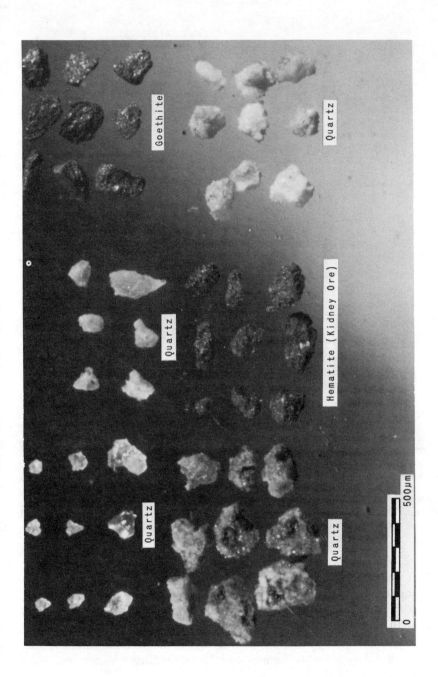

FIG. 8—*Sorted mineral grains from Minnesota taconite ore.*

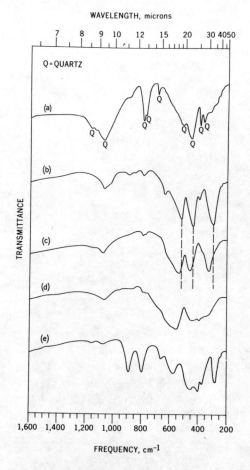

FIG. 9—*Infrared spectra of mineral grains from taconite ore from the Sherman Mine, Hibbing, Minn.: (a) representative sample; (b) hematite (kidney-ore), 400 μm reddish-brown granular grain; (c) hematite (specularite), 400 μm lustrous black grain from natural ore heated to 1000°C in hydrogen for 30 min.; (d) maghemite, 300 μm reddish-black grain, from natural ore heated to 1000°C in hydrogen for 30 min.; (e) goethite, 250 μm dull black striated grain.*

reduced by heating to 1000°C in hydrogen for 30 min, spectra of hematite grains were altered, as shown for example by curve *c* of Fig. 9, and now matched that of the specularite variety of hematite. The conversion of hematite spectra from the kidney ore-type to the specularite-type has been shown to be dependent on temperature and oxygen fugacity,[6] and we have made practical use of this phenomenon in deducing roasting conditions. Recent studies[7] have shown that the spectral differences correlate with changes in crystallite shape, which in turn may be produced from structural (bonding) changes in the hematite lattice.

Curve d of Fig. 9 shows the spectrum of a grain of cubic γ-Fe_2O_3 (maghemite), associated with trace amounts of quartz. The grain was isolated from the reduced ore sample, and the presence of this metastable ferric oxide, which forms as an intermediate phase in the reduction of hematite to magnetite, indicates nonequilibrium conditions during the roasting. Grains of hydrated iron oxide isolated from the natural ore (for example, Fig. 9, curve e) were identified as α-iron oxyhydroxide (FeOOH) (goethite). Its polymorphs, β-FeOOH (akaganéite) and γ-FeOOH (lepidocrocite), readily distinguishable by their infrared spectra[8], were not found. After the goethite grains were heated to 1000°C in hydrogen for 30 min, their infrared spectra matched that of the specularite variety of hematite. The heated grains showed little change in external morphology from those of the original goethite grains in the natural unheated ore pictured in Fig. 8.

Marine Minerals

Success in locating and utilizing ocean mineral resources depends on a knowledge of the processes of their formation[9], which can be derived from detailed studies of their mineralogies and internal structures. We have found that infrared microanalysis is uniquely applicable in determining the mineralogy of potentially commercial marine deposits. For example, we isolated individual grains from a complex marine phosphatic sand obtained from the continental shelf off southern California, and from their infrared spectra obtained a detailed mineral structure characterization. The spectrum of a representative sample of the sand was obtained by macrosampling methods and is shown as curve a in Fig. 10. Calcite and quartz are seen to be predominant, and absorption bands from these minerals completely mask the bands of the principal mineral of interest—carbonate-fluorapatite. Lehr et al[10] and Tuddenham and Lyon[11] have shown that the degree of carbonate substitution into the apatite lattice is variable and can be quantified by ratioing the average intensity of the carbonate absorption bands at 1453 and 1428 cm^{-1} (carbon-oxygen vibrations) to the intensity of the phosphate band at 602 cm^{-1} (a phosphorus-oxygen vibration). Such a structural variation may give clues on the conditions of formation of the apatite deposit. We, therefore, isolated pure single grains of the carbonate-fluorapatite from the sand sample and from the moderate intensities of carbonate bands in their infrared spectra, as shown for example in curve b of Fig. 10, were able to determine without interference from other associated minerals that there was a high degree of carbonate substitution. It was particularly important in this determination to eliminate interference in the 1450 to 1420 cm^{-1} region from other admixed carbonates such as calcite, which is abundant in marine sands. We also isolated grains of glauconite from the

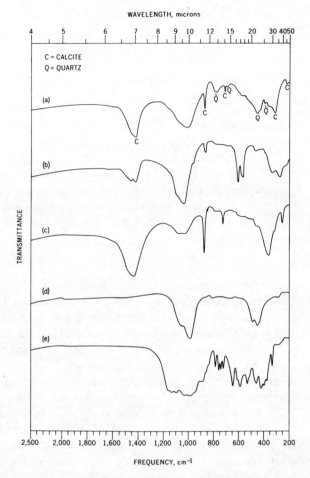

FIG. 10–*Infrared spectra of mineral grains from phosphorite sand from the Coronado Bank, Calif.:* (a) +200 –50 mesh sieved fraction, representative sample; (b) carbonate-fluorapatite, 300 μm brown milky resinous grain; (c) dolomite, 500 μm brown earthy grain; (d) glauconite, 350 μm dark green reniform textured grain; (e) albite, 500 μm milky green vitreous grain.

phosphatic sand and used infrared spectral-structural correlations to estimate the expandibility of this interlayered silicate. This structural variation in glauconite has been related to geologic age[12] and can be used to establish genetic relationships with other associated minerals in phosphorite samples. Manghnani and Hower [13] have shown that as the amount of expandable layers in the glauconite structure increases from 5 to 40 percent, the frequency of the most intense component of the silicon-oxygen stretching vibrations shifts from 990 to

1031 cm^{-1}. We observed a frequency of 987 cm^{-1} for this absorption band in grains isolated from the phosphorite sand (curve d, Fig. 10), which indicates less than 5 percent expandable layers, a well-crystallized structure, and late-stage glauconitization[13]. Single grain sampling also allowed a characterization of the structures of some accessory minerals in the sand, such as dolomite, (curve c), albite (curve e), pyrite, and garnets with varying magnesium-iron ratios.

In the studies on marine phosphates we also applied the nondestructive microreflectance techniques to determine the degree of carbonate substitution in the apatite of phosphorite nodules. For example, we obtained reflectance spectra from the sample shown in Fig. 11, for which several generations of nodule formation representing different mineralizations are distinguishable by irregular boundaries on its polished surface. Ratios of band intensities obtained from reflectance spectra of areas 1 through 6 indicated that the degree of carbonate substitution into the apatite lattice was higher in the darker areas. This was confirmed from absorption spectra obtained on material removed from the same areas as measured by reflection. Since Marlowe's studies[14] show that the darker areas of such conglomerates are older than the lighter areas, the subtle structural variation in the amount of carbonate substitution into the apatite lattice may aid in unraveling the complex imperfectly understood genesis of these marine deposits.

In other studies of marine deposits of commercial interest, we have demonstrated the necessity of applying infrared microanalysis to characterize structures of mineral grains occluded in ferromanganese nodules [15]. These complex mineral intergrowths are predominant in amorphous hydrated iron and manganese oxides which broaden infrared spectra and mask absorption bands of the small amounts of detrital minerals. However, as with phosphorite samples, we obtained single grain spectra that yielded information on specific mineral structures in these nodules, and the data were shown to be useful in comparing nodules from different geologic areas and in providing clues on their formation histories. In addition, molecular structure information on occluded mineral grains deposited contemporaneously with nodule formation may be correlatable with abundances of valuable metals (nickel, cobalt, copper) in the nodules, allowing predictions of enriched locations.

Minerals in Coal and Coal-Derived Products

An infrared characterization of the mineral constituents of coal, typically about 10 weight percent, is not easily obtained directly from spectra of the whole coal, because of interference absorption of organic structures. However, the low-temperature ash, obtained by electronic ashing of coal at 150°C, gives a well-resolved spectrum from which the predominant minerals can be identified. In previous infrared studies on minerals that occur in coal[16], we applied infrared macrosampling techniques which allowed a determination of only the

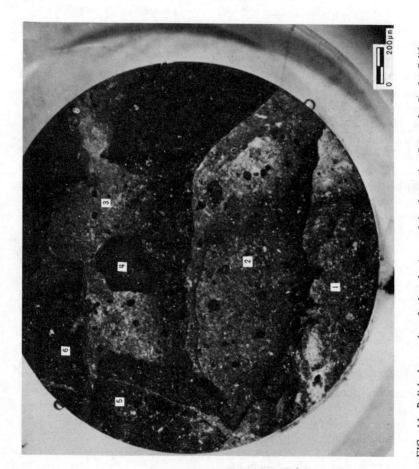

FIG. 11.—Polished sample of phosphorite nodule from the Coronado Bank, Calif., showing several generations of nodule formation.

predominant minerals from spectra of the fine-grained low-temperature ashes. However, when microsampling techniques were employed and spectra of pure mineral grains obtained, detailed molecular structure characterizations could be made, not only for predominant minerals but also for minor and previously undetectable trace minerals.

From a study of the structural alterations occurring in small grains of coal minerals during coal combustion, we have been able to deduce reaction conditions, as well as determine the mineralogy of the resulting fly ash. For example, in studies designed to develop new methods for electric power generation from coal (magnetohydrodynamics—MHD), it was necessary to determine the mineralogical composition of the fly ash produced when a mixture of bituminous coal and potassium carbonate (K_2CO_3) seed was fed to an MHD-type combustor. The spectrum of a representative sample of the fly ash, obtained by macrosampling techniques and shown as curve a in Fig. 12, reveals that the original coal minerals have altered to a mixture consisting predominantly of potassium sulfate (K_2SO_4) and a glass. We isolated single grains of these major constitutents and minerals occurring in minor amounts in this fly ash, and their well-resolved spectra yielded specific structural information from which reaction conditions could be deduced. For example, we derived a basic composition (50 weight percent silicon dioxide (SiO_2)) for the glass shown as curve b in Fig. 12, utilizing a previously developed infrared spectral correlation relating the frequency of the silicon-oxygen stretching vibration near 1000 cm^{-1} to silica content[3]. We determined by comparison of the spectrum of curve c with spectra of synthetic silicate standards, that some of the potassium from the admixed K_2CO_3 seed have formed kalsitite ($KAlSiO_4$). From the well-resolved spectrum of an olivine grain shown as curve d, we determined its iron (fayalite) content, utilizing correlations previously derived from synthetic standards[3]. From frequencies of absorption bands in the hematite spectrum of curve e (also showing a quartz band at 1075 cm^{-1}), and previously described spectral correlations[6,7], we determined that the temperature in some zones of the combustor reached 1100°C.

Acknowledgments

We thank the following persons from this laboratory for aiding in sample preparation and the collection of infrared data: A. A. Angotti, R. C. Berkshire, Jr., E. E. Childers, B. D. Stewart, and L. E. Makovsky. We thank R. Valdna, West Virginia University Chemistry Department, Morgantown, W.Va., for construction of the glass sorting stages; J. J. Renton, West Virginia University, Morgantown, W. Va., for assistance in designing the microsieving vial; G. A. Savanick, U.S. Bureau of Mines, Twin Cities Mining Research Center, Twin Cities, Minn., for supplying samples of taconite ores; and B. B. Barnes and L. W. Kimrey, U. S. Department of Commerce, National Oceanic and Atmospheric

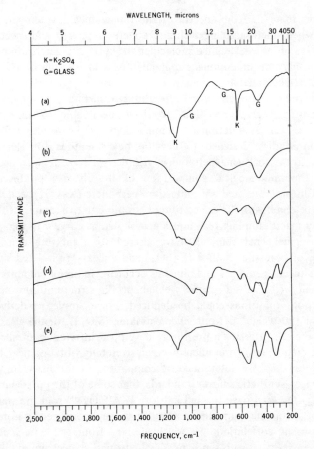

FIG. 12–*Infrared spectra of mineral grains from coal fly ash (MHD)*: (a) *representative sample;* (b) *glass, 300 × 170 μm orange fine-grained agglomerate;* (c) *kalsilite, 400 × 230 μm yellow opaque grain;* (d) *forsterite (Fa$_6$), 200 × 200 μm, light green translucent grain;* (e) *hematite, 400 × 250 μm red-orange rounded grain.*

Administration, Marine Minerals Technology Center, Tiburon, Calif., for providing samples of phosphorite and manganese nodules. Lunar spectra were obtained in work sponsored by NASA under Contract No. T-1760A.

References

[*1*] Estep, P. A., Kovach, J. J., Waldstein, P., and Karr, C., Jr., *Proceedings,* Third Lunar Science Conference, *Geochimica et Cosmochimica Acta,* Supplement 3, Vol. 3, The MIT Press, Cambridge, Mass., 1972, pp. 3047-3067.
[2] Estep, P. A., Kovach, J. J., and Karr, C., Jr., in *The Apollo 15 Lunar Samples,* J. W. Chamberlain and Carolyn Watkins, eds., Lunar Science Institute, Houston, Tex., 1972, pp. 470-474.

[3] Estep, P. A., Kovach, J. J., and Karr, C., Jr., *Proceedings,* Second Lunar Science Conference, *Geochimica et Cosmochimica Acta,* Supplement 2, Vol. 3, The MIT Press, Cambridge, Mass., 1971, pp. 2137-2151.

[4] Lyon, R. J. P., "Evaluation of Infrared Spectrophotometry for Compositional Analysis of Lunar and Planetary Soils," Stanford Research Institute, final report under contract No. NASr-49(04), published by NASA as Technical Note D-1871, 1963

[5] Lyon, R. J. P., "Evaluation of Infrared Spectrophotometry for Compositional Analysis of Lunar and Planetary Soils. Part II: Rough and Powdered Surfaces," Stanford Research Institute, final report under contract No. NASr-49(04), Technical Note CR-100, National Aeronautics and Space Administration, 1964.

[6] Estep, P. A. and Kovach, J. J., "Infrared Spectroscopic Studies of Hematite," presented at the Pittsburgh Conference on Analytical Chemistry and Applied Spectroscopy, Cleveland Ohio, 6 March 1971, program abstract number 294, p. 143.

[7] Estep, P. A., "Infrared Spectroscopic Studies of Hematite," M. S. thesis, West Virginia University, Morgantown, W. Va., 1972.

[8] Estep, P. A., Kovach, J. J., Karr, C., Jr., Childers, E. E., and Hiser, A. L., "Characterization of Iron Minerals in Coal by Low-Frequency Infrared Spectroscopy," in preparation.

[9] Barnes, B. B., "Marine Phosphorite Deposit Delineation Techniques Tested on the Coronado Bank, Southern California," *Conference Proceedings,* Offshore Technology Conference, Houston, Tex., April 1970, Vol. 2, Paper No. OTC 1259.

[10] Lehr, J. R., McClellan, G. H., Smith, J. P., and Frazier, A. W., "Characterization of Apatites in Commercial Phosphate Rocks," *Colloque International Sur Les Phosphates Mineraux Solides,* Toulouse, 16-20 May 1967, pp. 29-44.

[11] Tuddenham, W. M. and Lyon, R. J. P., *Analytical Chemistry,* Vol. 32, Nov. 1960, pp. 1630-1634.

[12] Hurley, P. M., Cormier, R. F., Hower, J., Fairbairn, H. W., and Pinson, W. H., Jr., *Bulletin,* American Association of Petroleum Geologists, Vol. 44, No. 11, Nov. 1960, pp. 1793-1808.

[13] Manghnani, M. H. and Hower, J., *American Mineralogist,* Vol. 49, Nov.-Dec. 1964, pp. 1631-1641.

[14] Marlowe, J. K., *Journal of Sedimentary Petrology,* Vol. 41, No. 3, Sept. 1971, pp. 809-827.

[15] Estep, P. A., "Infrared Microanalysis for Deducing the Formation History of Ferromanganese Deposits," Phase I Technical Report, International Decade of Ocean Exploration, National Science Foundation; also published as U.S. Department of Commerce NOAA Technical Report, 1973.

[16] Estep, P. A., Kovach, J. J., and Karr, C., Jr., *Analytical Chemistry,* Vol. 40, Feb. 1968, pp. 358-363, and Vol. 40, March 1968, p. 602.

H. K. Mao [1] *and P. M. Bell* [1]

Polarized Crystal-Field Spectra of Micro Particles of the Moon

REFERENCE: Mao, H. K. and Bell, P. M., "**Polarized Crystal-Field Spectra of Micro Particles of the Moon,**" *Analytical Methods Developed for Application to Lunar Samples Analyses, ASTM STP 539*, American Society for Testing and Materials, 1973, pp. 100–119.

ABSTRACT: Polarized crystal-field spectra of individual crystals, polycrystalline aggregates, and fragments of glass from the moon reveal fundamental information on their transition elements. Specifically, the oxidation states and structural coordination of iron and titanium in lunar samples are determined by a refined technique for measuring crystal-field splitting.

The quenched states of iron and titanium in lunar crystals act as fossil indicators of the chemical history of their crystallization. Spectral and other supporting data show that the rocks and soils returned from the Apollo missions have crystallized under extremely reducing conditions, on the order of approximately 10^{-13} atm of oxygen. Lunar glasses are also chemically reduced, and the absorptions of iron and titanium cause their green and red colors and influence their albedo properties.

Measurements of the shift with pressure of crystal-field bands of divalent iron in pyroxene suggest that pressure will enhance the properties of thermal transfer by radiation. Thermal radiation could be an efficient mechanism for heat flow in the lunar interior.

KEY WORDS: lunar analysis, lunar geology, crystals, optical spectrometers, lunar rock, high pressure tests, oxidation, reduction, iron alloys, titanium, glass

The present application of crystal-field theory is directly related to the initial discovery that spectral absorption lines of a free atom split into a multiplet of lines in magnetic (Zeeman effect) and electric (Stark effect) fields. Bethe[1][2] theoretically predicted splitting of lines that would be caused by nonspherical electric fields that surround atoms bound in a crystal. From measurements of the split bands one can deduce characteristics of the electric field surrounding an atom and determine its structural bonding and valence or oxidation state. Such was the main thrust of this study, many of the results of which have already

---

[1] Geophysicists, Geophysical Laboratory, Carnegie Institution of Washington, Washington, D.C. 20008.

[2] The italic numbers in brackets refer to the list of references appended to this paper. ·

been published[2, 3]. The object of this paper is to describe the methods of measurement, which have not been previously published.

The present method of observing optical spectra of single crystals at various pressures was developed from several techniques, many of them well known. Although the method can be employed with nearly any crystals, the lunar samples were particularly suitable, and some of the most recent results on lunar crystals are given to demonstrate the applications of the method.

Instrumentation

Collimated optical spectra, resolved over the range 255 to 3000 nm, were obtained from a Cary 17-I instrument. The diffraction grating was blazed at 750 nm, and the entire optical system of the spectrometer was designed to optimize the near infrared (NIR) region. For most of the present measurements, a tungsten-halogen light source was employed, and detection was made with a single lead sulfide (PbS) crystal or photomultiplier tube for the near infrared and visible wavelengths, respectively. A single diffracted beam is split for the analysis and the reference channels, when rejoined at the detector.

The optical elements (made from Infrasil) are curved compatibly with the slit system to favor performance in the NIR. The instrument, shown diagrammatically in Fig. 1, is designed for the special requirements of this study. The normal sample and reference chambers are not used but are replaced with a pair of matched rotatable Lambrecht-Glan polarizing prisms. The polarized beams emerging from this stage pass through a condensing lens system and are focused to a square plane image (30 μm, side) within the sample and reference. The beams then pass upward, through the tubes of matched Leitz microscopes, either to the detector or to the viewing oculars.

One can observe, measure, and align the sample and reference by setting the grating for some convenient wavelength in the visible region. In a spectral scan, chromatic aberration occurs, with the result that the beam becomes progressively defocused at long wavelengths. The system must be refocused every 150 nm of scan to maintain a 30-μm image.

Crystals are mounted and manipulated with spindle[4] and transfer[5] stages, so that the optical directions—α, β, and γ—can be properly aligned. To determine the optical absorption coefficient of a particular band, the same should be polished and the thickness measured precisely. This is important if the absolute intensity of a band must be known. In many instances, when the search for a band caused by a known mechanism is required, crystal fragments immersed in oils of suitable index of refraction suffice, and it is not necessary to prepare polished surfaces. Once the surface absorption is reduced, crystals of nearly any shape are usable.

High-pressure measurements are made in two ranges, 0 to 60 kilobars (kb) and 60 to 300 kb. For the lower range in which single crystals are employed,

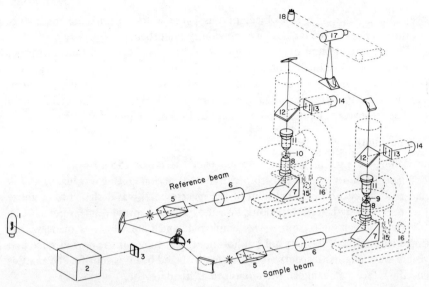

1. Tungsten-halogen light source.

2. Prism-grating primary and intermediate slit system of Cary 17-I
   spectrophotometer.

3. Exit slit.

4. Beam chopper and curved mirrors.

5. Glan rotatable polarizing prisms.

6. Auxiliary focusing lens system.

7. Mirror.

8. Condensing lens.

9. Sample.

10. Reference.

11. Objective lens.

12. Half mirror.

13. Polaroid analyzer.

14. Viewing ocular.

15. Substage adjustment (employs
    dial micrometer gauge).

16. Stage adjustment.

17. Photomultiplier tube.

18. PbS solid state detector.

FIG. 1—*Block diagram of apparatus for measuring crystal-field spectra.*

measurements are much the same as those at 1 atm, except that the crystal and
index-of-refraction fluid are contained and pressurized in a diamond-windowed
cell[6].

Control of the actual size of the transmitted beam and its chromatic
aberration becomes especially important in this apparatus because the diamond
window is only 250 to 400 μm in diameter. The crystal mounted in the cell is
much smaller.

Figure 2 shows an oriented crystal of lunar pigeonitic pyroxene in the high-pressure cell. The surrounding fluid is immersion oil of suitable index (refractive index = 1.5750 at 1 atm). Next to the pigeonite crystal is a small grain of potassium chloride (KCl), which is used for pressure calibration. (The KCl I-II transition can be observed visually when the pressure is raised to 19.3 kb.) The small dimension of the pigeonite crystal in the plane of the photomicrograph is 50 μm, and, because of the crystal's thin edges, the diameter of the beam must be restricted.

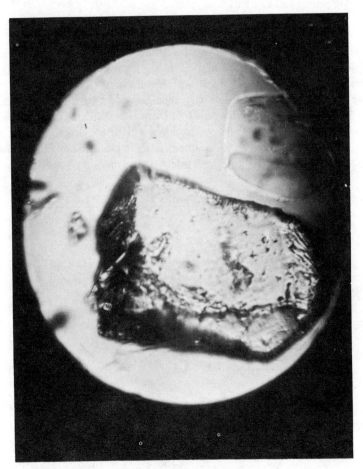

Large crystal, lunar pigeonite; small crystal, KCl; pressure medium, Cargille index-of-refraction oil; diameter of window, 250 μm.

FIG. 2—*Microscope view through diamond window of pressure cell.*

The procedure to determine the defocusing was to mask most of the focal spot with a 5-μm diaphragm and to map the actual dimensions of the beam at the plane of the sample. (The sample thickness was approximately 5 μm.) The change in image length as a function of wavelength (γ) is plotted in Fig. 3. The beam was refocused to its original size by adjusting the substage vertically. Changes were observed on a micrometer dial. The amount of vertical correction required is plotted as a function of wavelength in Fig. 4. The change of focal distance is controlled mainly by the chromatic aberration of the condensing lens (part 8 of Fig. 1) and is little affected by the chromatic aberration of the polarizing prisms and auxiliary lens (parts 5 and 6 of Fig. 1).

Lunar Crystals and Glass

The basic object was to identify the states of transition elements in lunar crystals in order to obtain information on the chemistry of their crystallization history. Lunar crystals and glass are chemically unique in terms of their zoning[7], but nonetheless they have apparently formed from lavas much like many of those already known on earth from Hawaiian and Pacific flows. The uniqueness of the crystals, in combination with the character of the Apollo igneous rocks, was such as to counter nearly all previously held views and predictions of the composition and origin of the moon and specifically of the

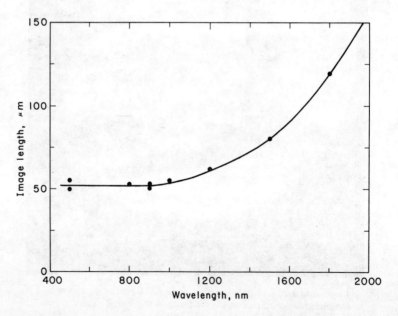

FIG. 3—*The change of length of the focused image of the exit slit system as a function of wavelength.*

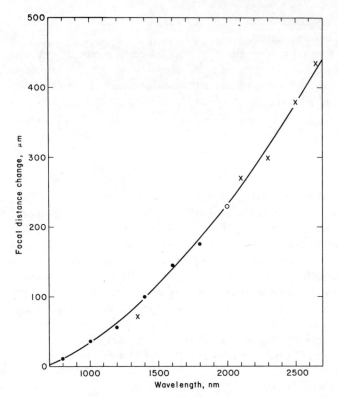

Open circles, setup as Fig. 1; solid circles, without auxiliary lens (part 6 of Fig. 1); crosses, without auxiliary lens and polarizing prisms (parts 6 and 5 of Fig. 1).

FIG. 4–*The change in focal distance of the substage condensing lens system, required to maintain a focused image, as a function of wavelength.*

lunar surface. The lunar crystals are sectorially and complexly zoned chemically, particularly in regard to the major elements, calcium, aluminum, silicon, iron, titanium, and magnesium, but also in regard to the minor and trace elements chromium, manganese, cobalt, and nickel. Early observers noted the coexistence of the free metal phases, iron and iron plus nickel in Apollo 11 rocks[8]. This factor supported the evidence of unusual chemical zoning and partitioning to suggest extremely reducing conditions of crystallization. Although free metals can be segregated commercially by routinely exposing terrestrial rocks to partial pressures of oxygen as low as 10^{-10} atm, free metals such as iron alloys in untreated terrestrial igneous rocks are rare.

The evidently anhydrous nature of lunar lavas has resulted in crystallization to a perfection unknown in terrestrial rocks. Lunar crystals are unaltered and are generally suitable for crystallographic study. In the present investigation of polarized crystal-field spectra, most measurements could be obtained on a single crystal or a glass fragment.

After spectral measurements were obtained, the crystals were analyzed for major and minor elements using the electron microprobe. Several points were analyzed on each crystal surface to test for chemical zoning. Analyses of all crystals and glass fragments referred to in the following discussion are given in Table 1.

Spectra

Pyroxene

The lunar rocks contain numerous transparent minerals, including pyroxene, olivine, and plagioclase. Absorption in terrestrial examples of these minerals has been discussed extensively by Burns[9]. The bands caused by iron are particularly intense in these minerals, and can be commonly detected when iron is present only in minor amounts (less than 1 weight percent). Figure 5 shows the spectra for a pigeonitic pyroxene crystal from an Apollo 12 rock (12063,79). The measurements were made with the present apparatus as part of a project involving calibration for remote spectral scanning of the lunar surface by telescope[10].

Using empirical assignments, the strong β band at 10 395 cm^{-1} (962 nm) and the weak a and γ bands nearby (10 395 cm^{-1}) are assumed to be caused by a spin-allowed transition in Fe^{2+}, influenced by the weak octahedral crystalline field. This site, designated M2 in pyroxene, is formed by the six coordinating oxygen ions. The bands at 4460 cm^{-1} (2242 nm) are also caused by transitions within the Fe^{2+} ion at M2, and polarizations correspond to the degree of distortion of the octahedral site. Bancroft and Burns[11], aided by Mössbauer data, interpreted the spectra and made band assignments, assuming the spin-allowed transition to be of the type $^5T_{2g} \rightarrow \,^5E_g$. They suggested that the absorptions of the γ and β maxima are caused by separate transitions from a common ground state in Fe^{2+}. Taking into account the selection rules, as constrained by the symmetry of the wave function for the individual electrons[12], the directional dependence of absorption fits well with the above interpretation. Broadening and departure from strict polarization could result from Jahn-Teller distortion or simply from the small degree of nonalignment of optical and electronic directions.

Another octahedral site in the pyroxene structure, designated M1, is less distorted than M2 but contains relatively much less Fe^{2+}. Nevertheless, it causes polarized absorption, which can be seen at 8285 cm^{-1} (1207 nm) in Fig. 5. The relative intensities of M1 and M2 absorption bands can be correlated with the degree of ordering of cations (in this case iron and magnesium). Other bands are located in the visible and near ultraviolet; for example, those occurring at

TABLE 1—Compositional data.

Sample	Phase	Cr_2O_3	MnO	FeO	Na_2O	MgO	Al_2O_3	SiO_2	CaO	TiO_2	K_2O	Total
12040,49	pigeonite	0.70	0.32	15.75	na[a]	23.63	1.27	52.55	3.85	0.52	na[a]	98.67
12063,79	pyroxene:											
	pigeonite	0.94	0.35	16.37	0.02	18.70	2.01	51.15	7.98	1.20		98.48
	augite	0.00	0.27	11.89	0.04	15.09	3.34	50.00	15.25	1.93		98.75
14163,33	plagioclase	0.14	0.01	0.43	1.85	0.25	31.46	48.64	16.84	0.11		99.59
14163,33-1	glass		0.15	9.07	0.09	12.69	17.37	47.53	10.28	1.83		99.15
14163,33-2	glass	0.57	0.29	17.01	0.22	14.72	9.94	48.54	9.20	0.60	0.08	101.09
14163,33-3	glass											
14163,33-4	glass											
14163,33-5	glass											
14163,33-6	glass	0.15	0.31	20.75	0.21	5.86	9.41	44.23	10.19	7.36	0.06	98.55
14163,33-7	glass	0.60	0.28	17.02	0.24	14.60	9.86	46.42	9.38	0.64	0.17	99.10
14163,33-8	glass	0.18	0.05	5.54	0.24	7.42	22.82	48.12	13.33	0.46	0.00	98.33
14163,33-9	glass	0.13	0.10	5.08	0.03	9.01	24.34	44.07	14.00	0.29	0.03	97.05
14163,33-10	glass	0.60	0.32	21.91	0.18	16.45	6.71	44.56	7.83	0.99	0.18	99.58
14163,33-11	glass	0.28	0.18	11.16	0.44	10.54	16.85	47.15	10.75	1.58	0.12	99.11
14163,33-12	glass	0.34	0.26	16.68	0.28	8.73	11.89	47.00	9.94	3.36	0.01	98.60
14163,33-13	glass	0.47	0.33	20.31	0.21	8.07	10.03	45.85	10.17	2.93	0.12	98.38
14163,33-14	glass	0.00	0.00	0.41	3.70	0.15	30.23	52.38	13.14	0.05	0.00	100.18
15555,205	olivine	0.33	0.38	32.97	0.00	29.92	0.05	36.22	0.36	0.03	0.00	100.26
15601,94-1	glass	0.42	0.26	17.65	0.18	9.49	10.10	41.42	10.42	9.19	0.00	99.13
15601,94-2	glass	0.31	0.24	15.39	0.03	12.12	14.47	43.17	11.54	2.13	0.50	99.40
15601,94-3	glass	0.27	0.15	9.56	0.49	9.02	16.65	50.47	10.50	1.52	0.03	99.13
15601,94-4	glass	0.27	0.19	11.55	0.14	11.55	17.11	45.10	11.08	2.44	0.00	99.46
15601,94-5	glass	0.17	0.17	9.44	0.03	10.77	22.19	41.19	13.63	1.37	0.00	98.96
15601,94-6	glass	0.59	0.29	18.66	0.10	16.83	7.72	45.98	8.57	0.41	0.00	99.15
15601,94-7	glass	0.60	0.30	19.00	0.15	18.16	7.74	46.82	8.17	0.45	0.48	101.39
15601,94-8	glass	0.26	0.16	9.03	0.57	9.14	16.62	50.78	10.25	1.38	0.22	98.67
15601,94-9	glass	0.12	0.10	5.76	0.49	6.53	25.40	47.57	14.59	0.82	0.00	101.60
15601,94-10	glass	0.62	0.30	19.72	0.14	17.93	7.58	46.92	8.27	0.43	0.01	101.91
15601,94-11	glass	0.34	0.23	14.50	0.04	11.11	15.28	46.37	11.14	1.05		100.07

[a] na = not analyzed.

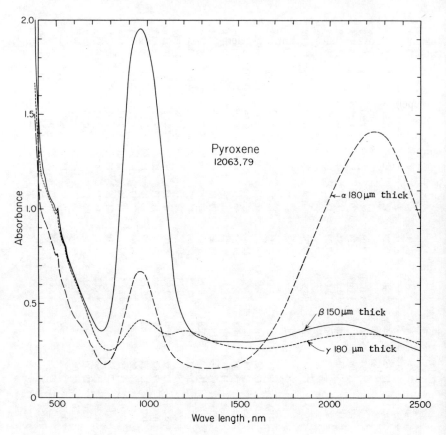

Central core, pigeonite; outer rim, augite. α, β, γ, optical directions.

FIG. 5—*Polarized crystal-field spectra of zoned lunar pyroxene from sample 12063,79 (after Adams and McCord [10]).*

approximately 14 900, 18 200, and 19 800 cm^{-1} (671, 550, and 505 nm, respectively). These bands are generally believed to be caused by charge-transfer processes or spin-forbidden transitions, and their assignment is uncertain. The band at 19 800 cm^{-1} is attributed to Ti^{3+}, although the absorption could be caused by a spin-forbidden band in Fe^{2+} [13]. At energies above 13 500 cm^{-1} (740 nm), the steep edge and its fine structure are caused by mixed charge-transfer bands of Ti^{3+} and Ti^{4+}.

The usefulness of these data can be appreciated if it is realized that information on composition, site occupancy, bonding, oxidation state, and coordination symmetry can be gained from one scan of the instrument. The band splitting (in electron volts) can be used to calculate the crystal-field parameter (Δ or $10Dq$). The crystal-field stabilization energy (CFSE) can then be calculated for the various transition elements in various states and coordinations. The values of CFSE give the relative destabilizations and can be used to predict the cation partitioning between coexisting phases[14].

The spectra of polycrystalline pyroxene samples do not give as much independent information as the spectra of single crystals because the absorptions must be averaged for an approximation of random orientation. Crystal-field bands in pyroxene shift with the amount of iron present, however, and the unpolarized spectra of lunar soils have been successfully related to the amount and composition of pyroxene they contain[10].

Olivine

Figure 6 shows the spectra measured for an olivine crystal from an Apollo 15 rock (15555,205). The coordination of Fe^{2+} in olivine is similar in many respects to that of Fe^{2+} in pyroxene, and the octahedral sites have the greatest effect on the spectral bands[9]. The Fe^{2+} ion in M1 causes the β absorption of 8680 and 11 210 cm^{-1}. Maximum absorption is caused by Fe^{2+} in M2, occurring at 9500 cm^{-1}. In the region 15 500 to 17 500 cm^{-1} the weak polarized band may be caused by Fe^{3+} (no more than a few tenths of a weight percent), but possible ambiguity with spin-forbidden bands at this energy prohibits making a firm assignment. The Fe^{3+} ion is believed to cause the apparent absorption edge starting at 19 000 cm^{-1} in terrestrial olivines, but this band has not yet been identified in the lunar counterparts. It is known that the true band-gap absorption in olivine is at energies in the midultraviolet region[2] and that the apparent edge could be caused by a charge-transfer process in Fe^{3+}. In less iron-rich lunar olivines, absorption bands possibly caused by Cr^{2+} have been observed[15], but titanium and nickel are absent or present only in trace amounts.

Plagioclase

The spectra of lunar plagioclase from Apollo rock 14163,33 are shown in Fig. 7. Polarized spectra of plagioclase have not been previously reported in terrestrial samples or synthetic analogues, and the assignments are not yet known. According to calculations from group theory[12], the strong polarized band at 8000 cm^{-1} is probably caused by pseudo octahedrally coordinated Fe^{2+}, which is present in minor amounts (ferric oxide (FeO) = 0.43 percent). Weeks et al[16] suggest that Fe^{3+} occurs in lunar plagioclase, on the basis of preliminary measurements of paramagnetic resonance. Possibly the existence of Fe^{3+} can be confirmed by the Mössbauer technique.

Glass

Fragments of glass mixed in with crystals have been found in most lunar soils. The bulk compositions of many lunar glasses are the same as those of lunar

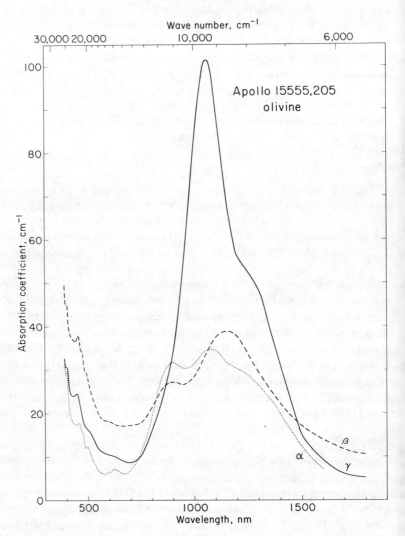

Absorption coefficient (cm⁻¹) is the absorbance per unit thickness of the crystal (in cm).

FIG. 6–*Polarized crystal-field spectra of olivine crystal from sample 15555,205.*

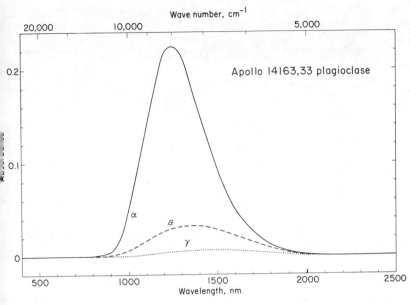

FIG. 7—*Polarized crystal-field spectra of plagioclase crystal from sample 14163,33.*

asaltic or anorthositic rocks, but some correspond to single-crystal composi-
ions. For example, the absorption band attributed to Fe^{2+} in plagioclase (8000
m^{-1}) can be seen in glass of the same composition but as a much broader band
9000 to 10 000 cm^{-1}).

The absorption bands in glasses of lunar rock compositions are caused almost
ntirely by iron and titanium, the effects of chromium and other transition
ements being too weak to be observed [3]. The spectra of three of these glasses
ith varying ratios of iron and titanium are shown in Fig. 8. Figure 8a shows the
pectrum of a relatively colorless glass spheroid, which has apparently formed
rom a contaminated melt of a low-iron basalt (5.09 weight percent FeO; 0.29
eight percent titanium dioxide (TiO_2)). A plot of the absorption of a typically
reen lunar glass is shown in Fig. 8b. The composition corresponds to that of a
igh-iron basalt with a low titanium content (17.01 weight percent FeO; 0.6
eight percent TiO_2), thought to be representative of the lunar mare
egions [17].

The spectrum in Fig. 8c is of a red glass high in both iron and titanium (20.84
eight percent FeO; 7.30 weight percent TiO_2), which also corresponds to a
nare basalt. Glasses colored brown contain intermediate amounts of titanium.

The strong band at 9000 to 10 000 cm^{-1} becomes more intense with
ncreasing iron content, but the energy of the band appears to remain constant.

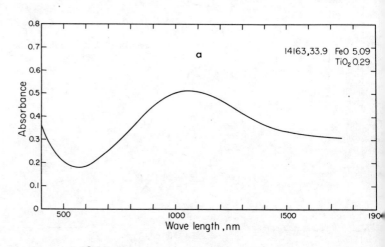

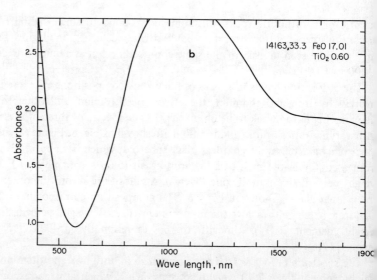

FIG. 8–*Unpolarized spectra of lunar glass fragments (after Bell and Mao* [3]).

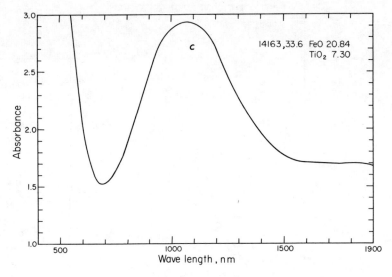

FIG. 8–*Continued.*

Titanium absorption in these glasses is probably affected by the ratio of Ti^{3+} to Ti^{4+} as well as by the total concentration of titanium. Actually, the main absorption band of titanium is in the ultraviolet region, at higher energy than that measurable by the present technique, but the low-energy shoulder tails into the visible region and combines with the high-energy tail of the Fe^{2+} band. The resultant absorption minimum is evidently related to the Ti^{3+}/Ti^{4+} ratio and the total amount of titanium but is not affected by the variation in concentration of iron in these glasses (5 to 22 weight percent FeO). In effect, this absorption minimum is a visible transmission "window," which determines the color and strongly affects the albedo properties of lunar glass.

Figure 9 shows a plot of the FeO content versus the absorption coefficient (absorbance per unit thickness, cm^{-1}) of the iron band of several lunar glasses. A small amount of scatter of the points is evident, but this is probably caused by errors introduced by the differences in shape of the glass fragments. The data for titanium given in Fig. 10 show much more scatter. The wavelength of minimum absorption in the visible region versus TiO_2, content is plotted for several fragments. The variation is a function of at least one variable other than the total amount of titanium (probably the Ti^{3+}/Ti^{4+} ratio). All points are on one side of the dashed line, which may correspond to a limiting value of P_{O_2} for the quenched liquids. If this is so, a line for the other limit will lie near the vertical axis, and curves corresponding to intermediate oxygen pressures will be between the two lines. The range of oxygen pressure for the two lines and for the glasses plotted between them is 10^{-7} to 10^{-14} atm [15].

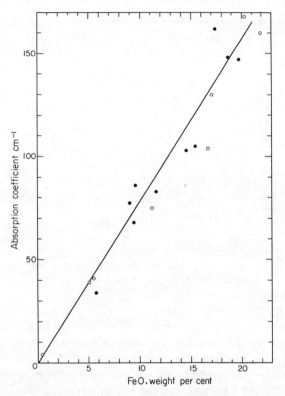

FIG. 9—*Plot of absorption coefficient (absorbance per unit thickness, cm⁻¹) of various lunar glasses from soil sample 14163,33 versus their iron content (after Bell and Mao [3]).*

The following factors can be summarized from these data[3]:

(*a*) The colors of lunar glasses are caused mainly by the variation of titanium and the Ti^{3+}/Ti^{4+} ratio.

(*b*) The band caused by iron varies in intensity with iron content but not in energy. Evidently the average atomic coordination site for iron is similar in all the glasses. This should be considered in spectral interpretations of the iron content of lunar soils, which are composed of both crystals and glass.

(*c*) The band caused by iron is in the near infrared, where it strongly affects thermal radiation. Lunar soils composed mainly of these glasses would possess uniform thermal properties, independent of the concentration of iron, because the absorption band does not shift significantly in energy.

Spectra Measured at High Pressure

The effect of pressure on the crystal field is important because the field varies with $1/R^5$ (R = interatomic distance). As the crystal field intensifies, the

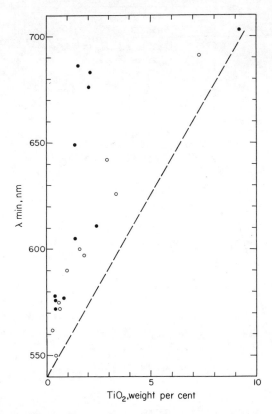

FIG. 10–*Plot of the wavelength of the absorption minimum between the shoulder due to titanium and the crystal-field band due to iron, versus titanium content (after Bell and Mao* [3]).

stabilization energy exerts a stronger control on the chemical partitioning of transition elements. The absorption bands shift in energy with pressure[18], and the thermal properties of crystals are affected as well.

Figure 11 shows an example of polarized crystal-field spectra of the pigeonitic pyroxene from lunar rock 12040,49 at 1 bar and at 20 kb. The main absorption band at 10 870 cm^{-1} has shifted to 11 019 cm^{-1}. Another pigeonite from the same sample was measured in polycrystalline form as shown in Fig. 12. The broad, nonpolarized Fe^{2+} band shifts from 10 667 to 11 351 cm^{-1} as the pressure is increased from 1 bar to 90 kb.

These experiments have just been started, and it will be necessary to obtain data on various transition elements before a stabilization series can be established. This will be similar to the one known for 1 atm[14], but it is likely that the change in stabilization energy with pressure will vary between transition

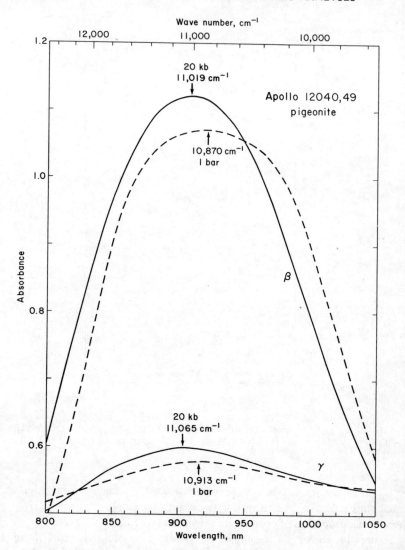

FIG. 11–*Polarized crystal-field band due to Fe^{2+} in pigeonite crystal from sample 12040,49.*

elements. It is significant that the iron bands shift to higher energy with pressure and tend to broaden the transmission in the near infrared. This is a "window" for heat transfer by radiation, which could be an efficient mechanism for heat flow in the moon's interior. The temperature effect on the bands at these pressures is not known.

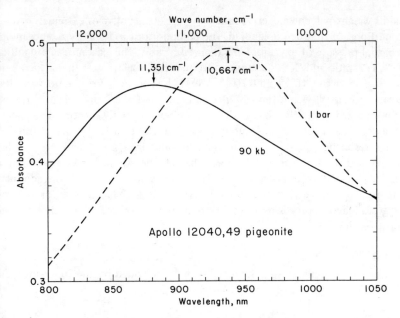

FIG. 12–*Unpolarized crystal-field band of polycrystalline sample of crystal whose* ʲlarized spectra are shown in Fig. 11.

ʲxygen Fugacity of Lunar Lavas

   The spectral measurements of these crystals from the ancient (3 to 4 billion ears old) lunar lavas sampled on the Apollo 11, 12, 14, and 15 missions can be ʲed to interpret the degree of oxidation during their cooling from molten ʲquid. The state of oxidation/reduction of transition elements in the crystals ʲpears to be "frozen in," and they act as fossil indicators of the chemical ʲvironment. Later alteration of the states by meteorite impact or perhaps by ʲe solar wind may obscure their original condition, but it is difficult to assess ʲcondary effects of this kind. Most of the lunar rocks do not show visible ʲvidence of shock damage, which would have been caused by severe impact, and ʲr the most part lunar crystals appear to be pristine and virtually unaltered. ʲven though extensive data on lunar rocks have not yet been obtained, ʲmplementary information, particularly chemical, can be used to support the ʲectral data.

   The fact that free metal alloys coexist in lunar rocks immediately suggests ʲat the mean partial pressure of oxygen in equilibrium at crystallization was less ʲan 10^{-7} atm. Lunar olivines are greatly depleted in nickel compared with ʲrrestrial ones, but the first metals to precipitate in lunar rocks contain as much as 40 weight percent nickel[19], which is also suggestive of extremely reducing conditions. If titanium is ignored, the compositions of lunar pyroxenes indica a partial pressure of oxygen of less than 10^{-11} atm. The existence of a significan Ti^{3+}/Ti^{4+} ratio and Cr^{2+}, determined from optical spectra, sets the oxygen parti pressure between 10^{-13} and 10^{-14} atm[15]. The Fe^{2+}/Fe^{3+} ratio is probab greater than 99.5. Although the presence of Fe^{3+} in olivine has bee hypothesized (on the basis of the present optical spectra data and « paramagnetic resonance measurements by Weeks et al[16]), data from Mös bauer resonance suggest the presence of only iron metal and Fe^{2+} in lun samples. It is now generally agreed that all the Apollo rocks are chemical reduced relative to terrestrial rocks. The cause is not yet clear. If the dominatir chemical system within the lunar interior was a reducing one, as the roc suggest, igneous processes on the moon must have been very different fro those on the earth.

Acknowledgments

We wish to acknowledge financial support provided by the following grant NASA, NGL-09-140-012; NSF, GP-4384 and GA-22707.

References

[1] Bethe, H. A., *Annalen der Physik,* Vol. 3, 1929, pp. 133-206 (English translatic Consultants Bureau, New York).

[2] Mao, H. K. and Bell, P. M., *Science,* Vol. 176, No. 4033, 28 April 1972, pp. 403-4C

[3] Bell, P. M. and Mao, H. K., *Proceedings,* Third Lunar Science Conference, *Geochim* *et Cosmochimica Acta,* Supplement 3, Vol. 1, The MIT Press, Cambridge, Mass., 197 pp. 545-553.

[4] Wilcox, R. E., *American Mineralogist,* Vol. 44, Nos. 11-12, Nov.-Dec. 1959, p 1272-1293.

[5] Chao, E. C. T. and Minkin, J. A., *American Mineralogist,* Vol. 55, Nos. 7-8, Sept.-O 1970, pp. 1416-1423.

[6] Mao, H. K. and Bell, P. M., *Carnegie Institution of Washington Year Book,* No. 7 1971, pp. 207-215.

[7] Boyd, F. R. and Smith, D., *Journal of Petrology,* Vol. 12, No. 3, 1971, pp. 439-4C

[8] Lunar Sample Preliminary Examination Team, (LSPET) *Science,* Vol. 165, No. 389 19 Sept. 1969, p. 1211.

[9] Burns, R. G., *Mineralogical Applications of Crystal Field Theory,* University Pre Cambridge, England, 1970.

[10] Adams, J. B. and McCord, T., *Proceedings,* Third Lunar Science Conferen *Geochimica et Cosmochimica Acta,* Supplement 3, Vol. 3, The MIT Press, Cambridg Mass., 1972, pp. 3021-3034.

[11] Bancroft, G. M. and Burns, R. G., *American Mineralogist,* Vol. 52, Nos. 9- Sept.-Oct. 1967, pp. 1278-1287.

[12] Cotton, F. A., *Chemical Applications of Group Theory,* Interscience, New York, 196

[13] Burns, R. G., Abu-Eid, R. M., and Huggins, F. E. in *Lunar Science III,* Carol Watkins, ed., Lunar Science Institute, Contribution No. 88, Houston, 1972, p. 108.

[14] Curtis, C. D., *Geochimica et Cosmochimica Acta,* Vol. 28, Mar. 1964, pp. 389-402.

[15] Haggerty, S. E., Boyd, F. R., Bell, P. M., Finger, L. W., and Bryan, W. B., *Science,* V 167, No. 3918, 30 Jan. 1970, pp. 613-615.

[16] Weeks, R. A., Kolopus, J. L., and Kline, D. in *Lunar Science III,* Carolyn Watkins, ed., Lunar Science Institute, Contribution No. 88, Houston, 1972, p. 791.

[17] Reid, A., Ridley, W., Warner, J., Harmon, R., Brett, R., Jakes, P., and Brown, R. in *Lunar Science III,* Carolyn Watkins, ed., Lunar Science Institute, Contribution No. 88, Houston, 1972, p. 640.

[18] Bell, P. M. and Mao, H. K., *Carnegie Institution of Washington Year Book,* No. 68, 1970, pp. 253-256.

[19] Taylor, L. A., Kullerud, G., and Bryan, W. B., *Proceedings,* Second Lunar Science Conference, *Geochimica et Cosmochimica Acta,* Supplement 2, Vol. 1, The MIT Press, Cambridge, Mass., 1971, pp. 855-871.

A. Volborth,[1] *R. Dayal,*[1] *P. McGhee,*[1] *and S. Parikh* [1]

Method for Ultra-Accurate Oxygen Determination for Rare Reference Samples

REFERENCE: Volborth, A., Dayal, R., McGhee, P., and Parikh, S., "**Method for Ultra-Accurate Oxygen Determination for Rare Reference Samples,**" *Analytical Methods Developed for Application to Lunar Samples Analyses, ASTM STP 539,* American Society for Testing and Materials, 1973, pp. 120–150.

ABSTRACT: Lunar rocks are deficient in oxygen. In order that a meaningful analysis of oxygen could be performed on lunar, meteoritic, and terrestrial rocks a high degree of accuracy is needed. Because of the rarity of such samples the method selected has to be nondestructive.

A highly accurate fast-neutron activation method that permits nondestructive analysis of lunar, meteoritic, and terrestrial rocks is described. It consists of a dual cross-transfer system that corrects for all electronic drifts and surges as well as for neutron beam fluctuation. This method uses chemically different reference samples: silica, aluminum oxide, ferric oxide, calcium carbonate, and their carefully prepared mixtures of which infrared spectra are first taken to ascertain complete absence of water and hydroxyl groups. Accurate oxygen values are reported for six U.S. Bureau of Standards standard reference materials: opal glass, bauxite, Na-feldspar, argillaceous limestone, dolomitic limestone, and the phosphate rock; the U.S. Geological Survey biotite LP-6; and the Smithsonian Institution "Allende meteorite."

KEY WORDS: lunar analysis, lunar geology, oxygen analysis, fast neutrons, lunar rock, standards, meteorites, rocks, stoichiometry

Possible deficiency in oxygen in lunar rock samples was established during the First [1,2],[2] and Second [3] Lunar Conferences. Oxygen content is one major factor in stoichiometric calculation of silicate analysis [4]. It provides an independent parameter needed especially when the material analyzed contains elements with multiple valencies (for example, iron, titanium, manganese), and metallic or sulfide phases as is the case in meteorites. In order to benefit from the oxygen determination, accuracy in the order of one part in 500 parts is

---

[1] Professor of geology, graduate student, research assistant, and chemist, respectively, Dalhousie University, Halifax, N.S., Canada.

[2] The italic numbers in brackets refer to the list of references appended to this paper.

necessary. Oxygen determination with a standard deviation of ± 0.1 percent at oxygen concentration of about 47 percent is required. Comparison of the specimens taken from unknown samples to chemically different known reference standards should yield a good check of the accuracy of such a method. The method is applied to dried U.S. Bureau of Standards (USBS) Standard Reference Materials No: 91 (opal glass), 69A (bauxite), 99a (Na-feldspar), 70a (K-feldspar), 1b (argillaceous limestone), 88a (dolomitic limestone), 120a (phosphate rock); the U.S. geological survey (USGS) biotite LP-6; and the first meteorite standard, the "Allende meteorite" prepared by the Smithsonian Institution of Washington.

This work is a refinement of earlier similar work by Volborth [5-7], and an attempt to provide the chemist with reliable oxygen values on samples which are generally available and are of complex nature so that a geochemist also may use them as reference. We also want to show that materials of quite different chemical composition can be used as secondary standards and give very good accuracy when carefully prepared. The Allende meteorite [8] analysis is then used as an example in such an approach to oxygen determination in extraterrestrial material. The ultimate goal of this work is to show that very accurate oxygen data could be retrieved from lunar materials.

Equipment

The equipment used consisted of the Kaman A-711 sealed tube neutron generator and a Kaman special sample transfer system where samples are rotated around two perpendicular axes in front of the target and are switched to opposite positions on alternate runs. The logic of such a system and its selfcorrecting nature were described by Volborth in 1966[6]; an identical logic of a more complex system was described by Priest[9]. Our present system at Dalhousie uses 3-in. sodium iodide detectors and Ortec 113-preamplifier, 451-spectroscopy amplifier, 420A-timing single channel analyzer, 430 high speed scaler, and automatic printout combination electronics controlled through a teletype which also controls a PDP-8 computer and Nuclear Data 50/50 MCA-system.

Specimens

Specimens of the standard materials were dried at $110°C$, cooled in a desiccator, packed tightly into "rabbits," and sealed. Our secondary oxide and carbonate reference samples were prepared similarly after ignition in oxygen atmosphere. The secondary reference samples were silica (SiO_2) (quartz), aluminum oxide (Al_2O_3), ferric oxide (Fe_2O_3), calcium carbonate ($CaCO_3$), and known mixtures of SiO_2, Al_2O_3, and Fe_2O_3. Potassium bromide (KBr) pellets were then prepared and infrared spectra taken to ascertain complete absence of water and OH-groups in these samples. It was found during this

TABLE 1–*Oxygen content in standard reference materials.*

Sample	Standards	Total Counts	Oxygen, %
NBS-91 opal glass	SiO_2	1 700 000	46.15
NBS-91 opal glass	$SiO_2 + Al_2O_3$	500 000	45.85
NBS-91 opal glass	$SiO_2 + Al_2O_3 + Fe_2O_3$	1 000 000	45.98
NBS-91 opal glass	$Al_2O_3 ; Fe_2O_3$	800 000	45.96
		Mean	45.99 ± 0.12
		$-F = 0$	2.94
			43.05
NBS-99a Na-feldspar	SiO_2	400 000	48.03
NBS-99a Na-feldspar	$SiO_2 + Al_2O_3$	800 000	48.09
NBS-99a Na-feldspar	$SiO_2 + Al_2O_3 + Fe_2O_3$	800 000	48.23
NBS-99a Na-feldspar	$Al_2O_3 ; Fe_2O_3$	800 000	47.94
			48.07 ± 0.12
NBS-70a K-feldspar	SiO_2	800 000	47.65
NBS-70a K-feldspar	Al_2O_3	1 600 000	47.50
NBS-70a K-feldspar	$SiO_2 + Al_2O_3$	800 000	47.39
NBS-70a K-feldspar	$SiO_2 + Al_2O_3 + Fe_2O_3$	800 000	47.53
NBS-70a K-feldspar	Fe_2O_3	400 000	47.38
			47.49 ± 0.11
NBS-69A bauxite	SiO_2	1 300 000	58.28
NBS-69A bauxite	$SiO_2 + Al_2O_3$	1 500 000	57.92
NBS-69A bauxite	$SiO_2 + Al_2O_3 + Fe_2O_3$	800 000	58.06
NBS-69A bauxite	$Al_2O_3 ; Fe_2O_2$	1 000 000	57.97
			58.06 ± 0.16
NBS-lb argillaceous limestone	SiO_2	1 200 000	49.61
NBS-lb argillaceous limestone	$SiO_2 + Al_2O_3$	800 000	49.12
NBS-lb argillaceous limestone	$SiO_2 + Al_2O_3 + Fe_2O_3$	800 000	49.62
NBS-lb argillaceous limestone	$Al_2O_3 ; Fe_2O_3$	1 300 000	49.20
NBS-lb argillaceous limestone	$CaCO_3$	800 000	49.56
			49.42 ± 0.24
NBS-88a dolomitic limestone	SiO_2	1 000 000	51.58
NBS-88a dolomitic limestone	$SiO_2 + Al_2O_3$	500 000	51.22
NBS-88a dolomitic limestone	$SiO_2 + Al_2O_3 + Fe_2O_3$	800 000	51.52

TABLE 1 –(*Continued*).

Sample	Standards	Total Counts	Oxygen, %
NBS-88a dolomitic limestone	Al_2O_3	400 000	51.50
NBS-88a dolomitic limestone	$CaCO_3$	1 000 000	51.21
			51.41 ± 0.18
NBS-120a phosphate rock	SiO_2	800 000	41.81
NBS-120a phosphate rock	$SiO_2 + Al_2O_3$	700 000	41.71
NBS-120a phosphate rock	$SiO_2 + Al_2O_3 + Fe_2O_3$	800 000	41.83
NBS-120a phosphate rock	$Al_2O_3 ; Fe_2O_3$	800 000	41.56
			41.73 ± 0.12
		$-F = 0$	2.01
			39.72
USGS biotite LP-6 (Feb. 2/72), dried 110 deg	SiO_2	300 000	44.00
USGS biotite LP-6 (Feb. 2/7), dried 110 deg	$SiO_2 + Al_2O_3$	300 000	43.46
USGS biotite LP-6 (Feb. 2/72), dried 110 deg	$SiO_2 + Al_2O_3 + Fe_2O_3$	500 000	43.74
USGS biotite LP-6 (Feb. 2/72), dried 110 deg	$Al_2O_3 ; Fe_2O_3$	500 000	44.09
			43.82 ± 0.28
USGS biotite LP-6 (March 22/72) dried 110 deg	SiO_2	300 000	44.18
USGS biotite LP-6 (March 22/72) dried 110 deg	$SiO_2 + Al_2O_3$	300 000	43.99
USGS biotite LP-6 (March 22/72) dried 110 deg	$SiO_2 + Al_2O_3 + Fe_2O_3$	300 000	44.59
USGS biotite LP-6 (March 22/72) dried 110 deg	$Al_2O_3 ; Fe_2O_3$	300 000	43.53
			44.07 ± 0.41
USGS biotite LP-6 (March 24/72) against newly prepared standards	SiO_2	400 000	43.76
USGS biotite LP-6 (March 24/72) against newly prepared standards	Al_2O_3	400 000	43.57
			43.66 ± 0.13
Mean all biotite on 3 different dates			43.85 ± 0.21

sample preparation and preliminary neutron activation that many "pure" oxides (for example, lanthanum oxide (La_2O_3), titanium dioxide (TiO_2), and alkali carbonates) could not be equilibrated with the precision and accuracy needed. The main interference was carbon dioxide from the atmosphere and hygroscopicity. Such oxides and carbonates were then dropped from the list of stoichiometric mutually calibrated compounds chosen.

Experimental Procedure

The analytical procedure consisted of calibration of our chosen secondary reference samples comparing relative counting rate intensities with theoretical relative oxygen concentrations. This comparison resulted in linear calibration curves of 45-deg slope for 700 to 1800-mg oxygen representing the range of all our samples. Possible dead-time effects in the counters were studied and shown to be negligible at the highest counting rates used.

During the experiment specimens were irradiated and counted simultaneously, returned to loading port, switched, and the procedure repeated automatically adding the totals till at least 400 000 counts were accumulated per sample pair (σ = 632 counts, C = 0.16 percent). Because the data on the same specimen were accumulated in alternate electronic signal-processing systems, the ratio of the total counts of the pairs could be assumed to be corrected for electronic fluctuation and to represent the true ratio of oxygen in the samples. The oxygen percentage was then calculated by using this ratio as a factor. Each such self-correcting sequence of 8 or more activations that produced more than 400 000 total counts was considered an observation. In order to average all possible small weighing and sample preparation errors, usually each of the U.S. Bureau of Standards' reference specimens was compared to four chemically identical secondary reference samples or similar sample groups. The mean percentages of oxygen given in Table 1 represent therefore 1 000 000 counts or more each. For the purpose of showing the accuracy of this method and to avoid the presentation of long lists of numbers only data based on our chemically different secondary reference materials are compared, and the standard deviations given are based on these percentages. Such presentation is more rigorous than in our previous work[6] because it assumes stoichiometry of chemically entirely different substances.

In the case of the Allende meteorite[8] an additional set of secondary reference samples was prepared. These were called Standard 187, consisting of a mixture of 20 percent Al_2O_3 20 percent Fe_2O_3, and 60 percent SiO_2; Standard 183 consisting of 50 percent Al_2O_3 and 50 percent SiO_2; and Standard 184, consisting of 30 percent Al_2O_3 and 70 percent SiO_2. These mixtures were homogenized carefully, infrared spectra taken, and after packing into rabbits activation was performed on two separate splits of the Smithsonian Allende meteorite standard. Extreme care was taken in the analysis of these samples. The analysis was performed in an uninterrupted sequence on a Saturday-Sunday night when the net voltages fluctuation is minimum. Data and standard deviations of this determination are presented in Table 2.

It must be pointed out that data on oxygen approaching the reported precision in this paper have now been also achieved with single consecutive transfer systems[10,11]; however, in our opinion, the accuracy of such systems can never match that of dual systems such as ours, because of the difficulties in timing and calculations necessary to correct for neutron flux, voltage, and other fluctuations during the single consecutive runs.

The suggested value for oxygen in the two Allende meteorite splits is 36.51 ± 0.14 percent. It must be emphasized here that the Allende powders were not dried before packing as all the other powders here analyzed. This was because no hygroscopic water ($-H_2O$) had been detected by previous analysts[8] and because there was the danger of oxidation of iron during prolonged exposure to the atmosphere during heating.

In order to correct for the interfering F^{19} (n,a) N^{16} reaction[5], an accurate factor to be applied to known fluorine concentration was also determined. It differs from the value of 0.415 reported by us earlier[7]. The procedure consisted in irradiating simultaneously stoichiometric $CaCO_3$ with chemically pure ignited calcium fluorite (CaF_2) and calculating the oxygen equivalent of fluorine present. (Note that both are calcium salts and carbon does not react with fast neutrons.) To check the validity of this correction three quartz powder samples were prepared containing 4.87, 2.43, and 0.49 percent fluorine. Using the determined factor, which is 0.514 ± 0.004 (percent fluorine X 0.514 = percent oxygen), the following true oxygen percentages were calculated in the above samples: 47.94, 50.60, and 52.73. The determined oxygen by our method in the same sequence was: 48.07, 50.63, and 52.89 percent.

TABLE 2–*Oxygen in Allende meteorite.*

Sample	Composition of Standard		Counts	Oxygen, %
Split 19, Position 14	No. 187, 20% Al_2O_3, 20% Fe_2O_3, 60% SiO_2		1 000 000	36.41
Split 19, Position 14	No. 183, 50% Al_2O_3, 50% SiO_2		1 000 000	36.43
Split 19, Position 14	No. 184, 30% Al_2O_3, 70% SiO_2		1 000 000	36.32
Split 19, Position 14	No. 157, 100% SiO_2		1 000 000	36.30
		Mean		36.37 ± 0.06
Split 8, Position 26	No. 187, 20% Al_2O_3, 20% Fe_2O_3, 60% SiO_2		1 000 000	36.47
Split 8, Position 26	No. 183, 50% Al_2O_3, 50% SiO_2		1 000 000	36.69
Split 8, Position 26	No. 184, 30% Al_2O_3, 70% SiO_2		1 000 000	36.65
Split 8, Position 26	No. 157, 100% SiO_2		1 000 000	36.74
		Mean		36.64 ± 0.12

To show that our other dry samples were not overheated, did not loose excessive water ($+H_2O$) or carbon dioxide, and were not oxidized, hygroscopic water was determined drying twice for 2 h at $110°C$ and is reported in Table 3.

When the same but undried materials were analyzed in identical fashion all but phosphate rock showed less total oxygen (0.1 to 0.4 percent) which indicates anomalous behavior and cannot be explained at this point other than by oxidation while drying or vigorous absorption of oxygen or CO_2 from air after or during drying. The greatest addition in oxygen was observed in dried biotite ($+0.37 \pm 0.1$ percent). It may be noted that this mineral has about 12 percent Fe_2O_3 (USGS personal communication, Ingamels).

Discussion and Conclusions

When an analytical method, such as the fast neutron activation method just described, yields very precise results, factors such as varying moisture and possible oxidation of iron have to be considered in evaluating the accuracy of the results. We believe that our results indicate that the possible effects of absorption of neutrons and gamma radiation in samples of different density and composition range investigated cannot play a major role. Otherwise the good reproducibility of the results reported would not have been possible. We did not work in nitrogen or argon atmosphere because using large well packed samples containing about 1000 mg of oxygen the atmospheric oxygen was calculated to affect possibly only the fifth digit. An interesting point that we are now pursuing is the small increase of total oxygen with drying of most of the samples, whereas just the opposite effect would be expected.

We believe that the main significance of this method is in giving highly precise and accurate oxygen values. This ability should enable chemists and geochemists to add oxygen, the major constituent, to the list of elements analyzed with care in standard materials.

The method will be of greatest value where nonstoichiometric multiphase mixtures containing elements in multivalence states and metallic fragments have to be analyzed. One of us (Volborth) is now applying this method to the analysis of lunar samples trying to determine the total effect of processes causing

TABLE 3–*Hygroscopic moisture in samples analyzed in weight percent ($-H_2O$).*

Opal Glass	Na-Feldspar	K-Feldspar	Bauxite
0.30	0.12	0.13	0.91
Argillaceous Limestone	Dolomitic Limestone	Phosphate Rock	Biotite
0.34	0.04	0.91	0.203

nonstoichimetry in these rocks. In general, it may be stated that systematic research of oxygen balance in inorganic compounds should be our next objective, and we are now proceeding in this direction.

References

[1] Ehmann, W. D. and Morgan, J. W., *Proceedings,* Apollo 11 Lunar Science Conference, Vol. 2, Pergamon, New York, 1970, pp. 1071-1079.

[2] Rose, H. J., Jr., Cuttitta, F., Dwornik, E. J., Carron, M. K., Christian, R. P., Lindsay, J. R., Ligon, D. T., and Larson, R. R., *Proceedings,* Apollo 11 Lunar Science Conference, Vol. 2, Pergamon, New York, 1970, pp. 1493-1497.

[3] Ehmann, W. D. and Morgan, J. W., *Proceedings,* Second Lunar Science Conference, Vol. 2, The MIT Press, Cambridge, Mass., 1971, pp. 1237-1245.

[4] Volborth, A., Fabbi, B. P., and Vincent, H. A., *Advances in X-Ray Analysis,* Vol. 11, 1968, pp. 158-163.

[5] Volborth, A. and Banta, H. E., *Analytical Chemistry,* Vol. 35, 1963, pp. 2203-2205.

[6] Volborth, A., *Fortschritte der Mineralogie,* Vol. 43, No. 1, 1966, pp. 10-21.

[7] Volborth, A. and Vincent, H. A., *Nuclear Applications,* Vol. 3, 1967, pp. 701-707.

[8] Clarke, R. S., Jr., Jarosewich, E., Mason, B., Nelen, J., Gomez, M., and Hyde, J. R., *Smithsonian Contributions to the Earth Sciences,* No. 5, 1970.

[9] Priest, H. F., Burns, F. C., and Priest, G. L., *Analytical Chemistry,* Vol. 42, 1970, pp. 499-503.

[10] Morgan, J. W. and Ehmann, W. D., *Analytica Chimica Acta,* Vol. 49, 1970, pp. 287-299.

[11] Morgan, J. W. and Ehmann, W. D., *Activation Analysis in Geochemistry,* Universitets forlaget, Oslo, 1971, pp. 81-97.

Morteza Janghorbani,[1] D. E. Gillum,[2] and W. D. Ehmann[1]

Application of 14 MeV and Cf-252 Neutron Sources to Instrumental Neutron Activation Analysis of Lunar Samples

REFERENCE: Janghorbani, Morteza, Gillum, D. E., and Ehmann, W. D., "Application of 14 MeV and Cf-252 Neutron Sources to Instrumental Neutron Activation Analysis of Lunar Samples," *Analytical Methods Developed for Application to Lunar Samples Analyses, ASTM STP 539,* American Society for Testing and Materials, 1973, pp. 128–139.

ABSTRACT: Two neutron sources, a Cockroft-Walton 14 MeV neutron generator and a Cf-252 neutron source, have been applied to analyses of lunar samples for major and minor element determinations. Instrumentation and details of the techniques employed are discussed. It is shown that most major and minor elements found in lunar samples can be determined via the technique of instrumental neutron activation analysis employing these two relatively inexpensive neutron sources.

KEY WORDS: lunar geology, neutron activation analysis, lunar analysis, neutrons, neutron sources, chemical analysis, analyzing

Analysis of precious samples such as lunar materials often requires techniques that are nondestructive in nature. Furthermore, such samples are often supplied in small quantities so that further splitting for replicate analysis becomes impractical. These requirements coupled with the need for a precise, rapid, sensitive, and specific method of elemental analysis in lunar materials can best be met by the technique of instrumental neutron activation analysis (INAA). Although radiochemical separations may be needed to attain the highest degree of sensitivity that neutron activation is capable of, INAA has a very high sensitivity for many elements[1].[3] With exercise of proper care subpercent relative standard deviations are routinely obtainable making this technique one of the most precise analytical tools[2]. Although rapidity is a very relative term,

---

[1] Visiting assistant professor and professor and chairman, respectively, Department of Chemistry, University of Kentucky, Lexington, Ky. 40506.

[2] Assistant professor, Ashland Community College, Ashland, Ky.

[3] The italic numbers in brackets refer to the list of references appended to this paper.

128

the technique of instrumental neutron activation analysis ranks among the most rapid methods of obtaining data on many elemental abundances in materials of geochemical interest. When used with high resolution Ge(Li) detectors, it also offers a high degree of selectivity and multielement capability.

Of the various sources of neutrons, only two have been widely applied to analytical studies. These are reactor thermal neutrons and neutrons generated by means of low-energy particle accelerators which have a characteristic energy of about 14 MeV[3]. Most activation techniques using a nuclear reactor employ the (n, γ) reaction, due to the large thermal neutron cross sections of most elements and the availability of high-thermal neutron fluxes in reactor thermal columns (typically 10^{12} to 10^{15} neutrons (n) cm^{-2} s^{-1}). Therefore, for most elements, reactor thermal neutron irradiations offer the highest sensitivity. However, nuclear reactor facilities are major installations, requiring a large capital investment and a substantial operating budget. For many analytical laboratories the absence of a reactor on site has discouraged the use of activation analysis, due to the time delays and costs associated with the use of a remote facility. Furthermore, in special cases such as oxygen analysis, application of (n, γ) reactions is not feasible.

On the other hand, energetic neutrons from low-energy particle accelerators (for example, Cockroft-Walton neutron generators) are capable of inducing a variety of nuclear reactions, such as (n,p) (n,n'), (n,a), and $(n,2n)$. In many cases, reaction cross sections for these reactions are large enough to make milligram level determinations quite feasible with neutron fluxes of about 10^8 to 10^9 n cm^{-2} s^{-1} [3]. Coupled with automatic transfer systems, these economical neutron sources have proved to be extremely valuable in analysis of samples of geochemical and cosmochemical interest, including lunar materials. In the special case of direct oxygen analysis this system is the only one in widespread use for routine, precise, nondestructive determinations. Some important limitations of 14 MeV neutron activation analysis are: rapid target depletion which makes the technique impractical for long irradiations to produce longer lived radionuclides, the need for special care in sample positioning during irradiation due to the nonuniformity of the flux distribution, generally low reaction cross sections (millibarns to hundreds of millibarns), and special shielding requirements for the energetic neutrons produced.

These limitations of 14 MeV neutron generators and the limited accessibility of nuclear reactors for most analytical laboratories enhance the desirability of the new moderate flux isotopic neutron sources. Of the various sources available, Cf-252 is the most promising. Spontaneous fission of this element with its relatively long half-life of 2.6 years releases on the average 3.76 neutrons having average energy of 2.3 MeV[4]. The recent availability of rather large Cf-252 neutron sources, their relatively simple shielding requirements, moderate cost, ease of neutron thermalization, and fairly high neutron flux make such sources very useful for major and minor elemental analysis of samples of geochemical interest.

This communication describes lunar sample analytical techniques employing a Cockroft-Walton neutron generator and a 1.25 mg Cf-252 neutron source at the University of Kentucky. These techniques permit rapid, precise, non-destructive major and minor element abundance determinations without use of a nuclear reactor facility.[4] The modest cost and space requirements for these two sources of neutrons place activation analysis within the reach of many smaller geochemical research groups.

Nuclear Reactions

Tables 1 and 2 summarize the nuclear reactions utilized in the analyses of lunar materials at the University of Kentucky. Potential interferences are also listed. These interferences are of two types: Type I—nuclides other than that of interest producing the same indicator nuclide used in the particular determination. Type II—interferences due to unresolvable gamma-ray peaks. The last two columns of Table 1 provide a list of interferences and their abundance ranges. It is evident that in most cases the correction factors are small for lunar samples. Two exceptions are the aluminum interference in the determination of magnesium and the silicon interference in the determination of aluminum. Type II interferences are minimized either by application of appropriate correction factors, or by use of high resolution Ge(Li) detectors. In our work Type II interferences are not found to be significant. These interferences have been discussed in greater detail by Morgan and Ehmann[5].

Instrumentation and Techniques

The 14 MeV neutron generator used is a Kaman Nuclear Model A-1250, equipped with a single sample transfer system. Three crystal controlled clocks (Nuclear Data 536CTB) and accessory solid state electronics control the various phases of each irradiation-delay-count cycle. Precise timing is very critical with such short-lived isotopes as ^{16}N. The pneumatic single transfer system and the sequential programming circuit is a solid state version of that described previously by Vogt et al[6].

The Cf-252 facility is a 1.25 mg (April 1971) encapsulated source in an irradiation chamber with four irradiation ports located around the source at a distance of 4 cm. The entire polyethylene irradiation assembly is suspended in a double-walled polyethylene tank filled with deionized distilled water (total capacity 1050 liters). Thermal neutron flux inside the sample ports is 3×10^7 n

---

[4] Major and minor elements found in lunar rocks are those whose abundances are 0.1 percent or higher. Most common elements in this group are: silicon, oxygen, iron, aluminum, magnesium, titanium, sodium, manganese, calcium, and chromium.

TABLE 1—Nuclear reactions employed with 14 MeV neutrons.

Element	Reaction	Isotopic Abundance of Target Nuclide, %	Cross Section, mb	Half-Life	γ-Energy, MeV	Interference	Amount of Interference[a]	Approximate Abundance Range of Interfering Elements[b]
Oxygen	$^{16}O(n,p)^{16}N$	99.8	33	7.14 s	6.13 7.12	$^{19}F(n,\alpha)^{16}N$ $^{11}B(n,p)^{11}Be$	0.4	30 to 340 ppm
Silicon	$^{28}Si(n,p)^{28}Al$	92.2	250	2.31 m	1.78	$^{27}Al(n,\gamma)^{28}Al$ $^{31}P(n,\alpha)^{28}Al$ $^{56}Fe(n,p)^{56}Mn$	0.002 0.48 0.00157	3.7 to 7.8% 200 to 900 ppm 11.8 to 15.6%
Iron	$^{56}Fe(n,p)^{56}Mn$	91.6	144	2.58 h	0.84	$^{59}Co(n,\alpha)^{56}Mn$ $^{55}Mn(n,\gamma)^{56}Mn$	0.23	1500 to 2400 ppm
Aluminum	$^{27}Al(n,p)^{27}Mg$	100	87	9.46 m	0.84	$^{30}Si(n,\alpha)^{27}Mg$ $^{55}Mn(n,\gamma)^{56}Mn$ $^{59}Co(n,\alpha)^{56}Mn$	0.023	17.7 to 20.6%[c]
Magnesium	$^{24}Mg(n,p)^{24}Na$	79	180	14.96 h	1.37 2.75	$^{27}Al(n,\alpha)^{24}Na$ $^{23}Na(n,\gamma)^{24}Na$	0.67	3.7 to 7.8%[c]

[a] The ratio of the apparent weight of the element sought due to the interfering reaction, to the weight of the element producing the interference. These values are for our experimental configuration, and some values will vary for different configurations.
[b] These data are from Ref 16 and are for Apollo 11 mission only.
[c] These corrections are made in our analyses.

TABLE 2—*Nuclear reactions employed with the Cf-252 neutron source.*

Element	Reaction	Isotopic Abundance of Target Nuclide, %	Cross Section (b)	Half-Life	γ-Energy, MeV	Interference
Manganese	$^{55}Mn(n,\gamma)^{56}Mn$	100	13.3	2.58 h	0.84 1.81	
Aluminum	$^{27}Al(n,\gamma)^{28}Al$	100	0.23	2.31 m	1.78	$^{28}Si(n,p)^{28}Al$
Titanium	$^{50}Ti(n,\gamma)^{51}Ti$	5.34	0.14	5.79 m	0.32	$^{50}Cr(n,\gamma)^{51}Cr$
Sodium	$^{23}Na(n,\gamma)^{24}Na$	100	0.53	14.96 h	1.37	$^{55}Mn(n,\gamma)^{56}Mn$ (single escape of 1.81 MeV)
Calcium	$^{48}Ca(n,\gamma)^{49}Ca$	0.18	1.1	8.8 m	3.08	$^{23}Na(n,\gamma)^{24}Na$

$cm^{-2} s^{-1}$. The Cf-252 facility is also equipped with a remote single sample transfer system similar to that used with the 14 MeV generator. A more thorough discussion of this system is presented elsewhere [7].

Preparation of Samples and Standards

In the precise determination of elements employing either the 14 MeV generator or the Cf-252 source exact positioning of each specimen in the neutron beam as well as the counting chamber becomes extremely critical. Therefore, for high precision work, it is absolutely essential to reproduce accurately the position and the size of both samples and standards. The technique used in this laboratory is that developed by Ehmann and McKown[8], where the specimen is placed in appropriate size low-density polyethylene tubing. The two ends are closed off with solid polyethylene rods and then heat-sealed using shrinkable polyolefin tubing. The tubing is then placed inside a two dram polyethylene vial (polyvial) and positioned properly by means of polyethylene spacers. The polyvial is in turn heat-sealed to ensure complete closure of the specimen. All samples and standards are prepared under dry nitrogen in a special dry box reserved for this purpose in order to eliminate oxygen and water absorption by the specimen. This is especially critical in oxygen determination of lunar samples due to the fact that they are oxygen deficient and could easily pick up terrestrial oxygen. All standards except the iron standard are either National Bureau of Standards (NBS) primary standards or U.S. Geological Survey (USGS) standard rocks assayed against NBS primary standards and used as secondary standards. Previous work has established the stoichiometry of these standards. For iron determinations reagent grade ferrous ammonium sulfate hexahydrate is employed. Table 3 lists the standards used in this work.

Determination of Oxygen

This determination is done by a multiscaling technique developed by Morgan and Ehmann[2]. Briefly, each specimen is irradiated for 15 s, allowed to decay for approximately 6 s, and multiscaled for 60 s using a dwell time of 0.8 s per channel. All gamma radiation below approximately 4 MeV and above 7 MeV is rejected by a single channel analyzer. During irradiation the neutron flux is monitored continuously by means of a gas-filled BF_3 counter. A special computer program is then used to calculate oxygen abundances. Details of calculations involved are given elsewhere [2].

Determination of Silicon

The amplified output of the detector assembly is connected directly to an analog-to-ditital converter of the ND 2201 analyzer. The discrimination and zero

TABLE 3—*Standard materials used in 14 MeV and Cf-252 neutron activation analysis.*

Element	Standard	Source	Treatment
Oxygen	potassium dichromate (99.98%)	National Bureau of Standards NBS #136b	none
	L-1, fused optical quartz	Dr. W. Blackburn Department of Geology University of Kentucky	(a) chunks cleaned ultrasonically (b) powdered
Silicon	L-1	Dr. W. Blackburn Department of Geology University of Kentucky	as for oxygen
	opal glass	National Bureau of Standards NBS #91	heated at 110°C for 1 h
Aluminum	potassium feldspar	National Bureau of Standards NBS #70a	heated for 2 h at 110°C
	opal glass	NBS #91	as for silicon
Iron	ferrous ammonium sulfate, reagent grade	Baker chemicals	none
Magnesium	dolomitic limestone	National Bureau of Standards NBS #88a	none
Others	BCR-1, W-1 standard rocks, powdered	U. S. Geological Survey	none

level settings were adjusted to analyze only the region immediately around the ^{28}Al photopeak, and a conversion gain for 512 channels is used so that analyzer dead time is only 1 to 2 percent. The actual elapsed counting period is kept constant and is timed accurately by means of a crystal-controlled timer. The live time is recorded in the first channel of the analyzer memory. Abundances of silicon are derived using a special computer program.

Determinations of Aluminum, Magnesium, and Iron with 14 MeV Neutrons

Each specimen is irradiated for 120 s, allowed to decay for 300 s to minimize the Compton background from ^{16}N and ^{28}Al. Samples are counted for 300 s with a 4 by 4 in. NaI(Tl) well-type detector, and the pulses corresponding to the 0.84 MeV peak are stored in one half of the ND 2201 analyzer memory employing "dual-singles" mode of operation. The spectrum is then punched on paper tape for processing. This energy region includes the photopeaks due to ^{27}Mg (from ^{27}Al) and ^{56}Mn (from ^{56}Fe) which are unresolved. After approximately 2 h the specimen is recounted, this time for 1000 s. The region corresponding to the 0.84 MeV photopeak is stored in the same half as before, but the region of the 1.37 MeV photopeak of ^{24}Na (from ^{24}Mg) is stored in a different half by means of a separate analog-to-digital converter (ADC). This mode of operation results in decreased analyzer dead time and, hence, improvement in timing. Both regions are then punched out on paper tape for computer processing. Calculations for elemental abundances are carried out by a program which operates as follows: the Sterlinski integrals[9] are computed for each of the two photopeaks (1.37 and 0.84 MeV). This results in three sets of integrals two of which are for the 0.84 MeV peak and one is for the 1.37 MeV region. The integrals due to the second counting for the 0.84 MeV peak (due to ^{56}Mn) are corrected for decay back to the time of the first count and are subtracted from the integral due to both ^{27}Mg and ^{56}Mn. The difference is the contribution due to activation of ^{27}Al. At this point three sets of integrals are obtained, each set corresponding to one element. The ratios of each integral of a given set for the sample to that for the standard is computed, and the one giving the smallest Sterlinski variance[9] is selected for abundance calculations. After these abundances are calculated the appropriate correction factors are applied manually to each abundance to correct for various types of interferences. The above description is necessarily concise; an in depth description of the computer program being beyond the scope of this paper.

Replicate runs are done on successive days to minimize buildup of longer lived radionuclides. Each run contains several standards for each element dispersed throughout the run to compensate for experimental fluctuations within the day. Of course, neutron flux for each irradiation is monitored during the irradiation, and all Sterlinski integrals are normalized to account for the flux variations during the run. For each run residual activity corrections due to the previous irradiations are applied to each specimen. Normally three independent abundances are obtained for each sample from which a standard deviation is calculated.

Determinations with the Cf-252 Source

Sample preparation techniques used are the same as discussed previously. For each run a set of samples and standards are irradiated for an appropriate length of time depending on the particular element of interest. The standards most commonly used so far are USGS standard rocks BCR-1 and W-1, employed as secondary standards. Each specimen is then counted with either Ge (Li) or NaI (T1) detectors are listed in Table 4. Manganese, aluminum, and sodium are obtained from a single irradiation. The specimen is counted after either 30 or 60 s delay with a Ge (Li) detector, and ^{28}A1 and ^{56}Mn spectra are recorded. The 1.78 MeV peak of ^{28}A1 and the 0.84 MeV peak of ^{56}Mn are used for abundance calculations. Typical net integrated counts obtained for 0.5 to 1.0-g lunar samples are 30 to 800 for aluminum and 2000 to 10 000 for manganese. The specimen is recounted after either 1 or 2 h decay with a 3 by 3-in. NaI (T1) detector and the 1.37 and 2.75 MeV peaks of sodium are used for calculating sodium abundances. Typical net integrated counts for the 2.75 MeV peak are 200 to 1000 depending on the specimen. The irradiation and count times used for aluminum appear to be too long. This is because aluminum is determined in the same irradiation cycle as manganese and sodium. Titanium determinations are made on separate irradiations. Conditions are as outlined on Table 4. The photopeak to background ratio for this element is quite small due to the relatively low capture cross section and isotopic abundance of ^{50}Ti and large Compton backgrounds due to manganese, sodium, and aluminum. Typically a few hundred counts are present in the photopeak after baseline corrections are made for lunar samples of the size listed above.

Although thermal neutron fluxes in all irradiation ports have been found to be identical to within ±3 percent, each sample is compared with a set of standards irradiated in the same irradiation port. For abundance calculations either Sterlinski[9] or total peak area (TPA) methods are applied. Comparisons of the two methods have been carried out by Baedecker[10] and are being currently

TABLE 4—Details of irradiation procedure used with the Cf-252 source.

Element	Irradiation Time, min	Decay Time, min	Count Time, min	Detector
Manganese	120	0.5 to 1.0	15 to 20	Ge(Li)
Aluminum	120	0.5 to 1.0	15 to 20	Ge(Li)
Sodium	120	60.0 to 120.	15 to 20	3 by 3-in. NaI (Tl)
Titanium	15	1.0	15 to 20	4 by 4-in. NaI (Tl) well type

conducted in our laboratory as well and will be reported after sufficient data are obtained. Typically two to four replicate analyses are used in computing the reported abundances.

Results and Discussion

Elemental abundances obtained by the two techniques discussed previously are summarized in Table 5 for two typical Apollo 14 samples. The reported error limits are one standard deviation of the mean. Oxygen and silicon abundances are means of 5 to 6 replicate analyses; those for aluminum, magnesium, and iron using 14 MeV neutrons are means of three determinations, and all others are means of 2 to 4 replicas except for sodium results, which for these specimens are single determinations. As evident from these results, oxygen determinations reproducible to a percent or less are obtained routinely with this technique. In fact, this technique is the only reliable method of direct nondestructive bulk oxygen determination employed today. Our oxygen results in lunar samples are generally slightly lower than those reported by Wänke et al[11]. Since our analyses are performed under dry nitrogen while his are not, this difference could be due to oxygen pickup. Experiments are currently in progress to test this hypothesis. Our other results agree well with those reported by others [11-13].

The sodium results are based on the 2.75 MeV photopeak of ^{24}Na and agree

TABLE 5—*Summary of elemental abundances for selected lunar samples*[15].

| | Abundance, % | | |
Element	Apollo 14 Breccia 14321,225A	Apollo 14 Basalt 14053,42	Method
Oxygen	43.1 ± 0.2	42.1 ± 0.2	14 MeV
Silicon	22.7 ± 0.1	22.2 ± 0.1	14 MeV
Magnesium	6.1 ± 0.4	5.0 ± 0.4	14 MeV
Iron	9.5 ± 0.4	13.0 ± 0.3	14 MeV
Aluminum	8.0 ± 0.2	6.8 ± 0.1	14 MeV
Aluminum[a]	(7.50 ± 0.14)	(6.35 ± 0.14)	Cf-252
Manganese	0.120 ± 0.001	0.189 ± 0.003	Cf-252
Sodium	0.74	0.40	Cf-252
Titanium	1.24 ± 0.04	1.93 ± 0.11	Cf-252
Calcium[b]	(7.1)	(8.0)	
Total[c]	98.6 ± 0.6	99.6 ± 0.7	

[a] 14 MeV results are preferred, see text.
[b] Obtained from Ref *14*.
[c] The contribution of other minor and trace elements is commonly an additional 0.4 to 0.6 percent in lunar materials.

very well with results from reactor irradiated samples also obtained by our group (unpublished data). The 1.37 MeV sodium peak generally yields results higher than the 2.75 MeV peak. This could be because of interference due to the single escape peak from the 1.81 MeV gamma ray of ^{56}Mn. Other interferences are also likely. More work is needed to establish the real nature of these interferences. Titanium determinations contain rather large error limits. This is explained, as mentioned previously, by the fact that the titanium photopeak is low energy, the cross section and isotopic abundance of ^{50}Ti are low, and the Compton background due to the higher energy peaks of manganese, sodium, and aluminum is quite high. Chromium interference with titanium is negligible in these samples. Results obtained for aluminum using the Cf-252 source are somewhat lower than those obtained by 14 MeV and are on the low side of those reported by others[11,13]. No satisfactory explanation for this observation can yet be given, and we prefer the 14 MeV aluminum data at this time.

Work is in progress to evaluate the feasibility of determining calcium in lunar materials by means of Cf-252 activation. Determination of this element with the present available flux is difficult due to the very unfavorable isotopic abundance of ^{48}Ca and the low efficiency for detection of the high-energy gamma radiation. A further complication arises due to proximity of the much larger 2.75 MeV peak of ^{24}Na and the sum peak due to ^{56}Mn. With a 5 to 10 mg Cf-252 source calcium determinations in small lunar samples would be feasible. As evident from Table 5, the total of these abundances adds up to 100 percent within the experimental uncertainties involved. Since the calcium values were taken from literature they could be somewhat different for the actual samples reported in this work explaining the slightly lower values for totals for the Apollo 14 breccia.

Conclusion

It has been shown that the use of a 14 MeV neutron generator and a Cf-252 isotopic neutron source can provide reliable data for most major and minor elements in lunar materials and other samples of geochemical and cosmochemical interest. More work needs to be done to establish the nature and degree of interferences involved in some cases of Cf-252 activation. These sources of neutrons are within the cost range of many other types of analytical instrumentation and do not require extensive support facilities or laboratory space. Hence, the rapid and nondestructive features of activation analysis can be available to those not fortunate enough to have ready access to a high-flux nuclear reactor. Clearly, if trace element analyses are required, reactor irradiations or the use of conventional, but often destructive, analytical techniques would be required.

Acknowledgment

This work has been supported in part by National Aeronautics and Space Administration NASA Grant NGR 18-001-058. The cooperation of the University of Kentucky Computing Center and the assistance of J. M. Storm in the laboratory operations are gratefully acknowledged.

References

[1] Periodic Table of Elements, Activation Analysis Sensitivities, Gulf General Atomic, Inc., San Diego, Calif.

[2] Morgan, J. W. and Ehmann, W. D., *Analytica Chimica Acta,* Vol. 49, 1970, pp. 287-299.

[3] Ehmann, W. D., *Fortschritte der Chemischen Forschung,* Vol. 14, No. 1, 1970, pp. 49-91.

[4] *Californium-252, Its Use and Market Potential,* U.S. Atomic Energy Commission, 1969, p.13.

[5] Morgan, J. W. and Ehmann, W. D., *Proceedings,* NATO Advisory Study Institute, *Activation Analysis in Geochemistry and Cosmochemistry,* A. O. Brumfelt and E. Steinnes, eds., Universitets forlaget, Oslo, Norway, 1971, pp. 81-97.

[6] Vogt, J. R., Whmann, W. D., and McEllistrem, M. T., *Journal of Applied Radiation and Isotopes,* Vol. 16, 1965, pp. 573-580.

[7] Janghorbani, M., Sya, C. L., and Ehmann, W. D., *Proceedings,* American Nuclear Society, *Topical Meeting-Applications of Californium-252,* Austin, Tex., 11-13 Sept. 1972, in press.

[8] Ehmann, W. D. and McKown, D. M., *Analytical Chemistry,* Vol. 40, 1968, p. 1758.

[9] Sterlinski, S., *Analytical Chemistry,* Vol. 40, 1968, pp. 1995-1998.

[10] Baedecker, P. A., *Analytical Chemistry,* Vol. 43, 1971, pp. 405-410.

[11] Wanke, H., Baddenhousen, H., Balacescu, A., Teschke, F., Spettel, B., Dreibus, G., Quijano, M., Kruse, H., Wlotzka, F., and Begemann, F. in *Lunar Science III,* Carolyn Watkins, ed., Lunar Science Institute, Contribution No. 88, 1972, pp. 779-781.

[12] Morrison, G. H., Gerard, J. T., Potter, N. M., Ganjadharam, E. V., Rothenberg, A. M., and Burdo, R. A., *Proceedings,* Second Lunar Science Conference, *Geochimica et Cosmochimica Acta,* Supplement 2, Vol. 2, The MIT Press, Cambridge, Mass., 1971, pp. 1169-1176.

[13] Laul, J. C., Boynton, W. V., and Schmitt, R. A. in *Lunar Science III,* Carolyn Watkins, ed., Lunar Science Institute, Contribution No. 88, 1972, pp. 480-482.

[14] Compston, W., Vernon, M. J., Berry, H., Rudowski, R., Gray, C. M., and Ware, N. in *Lunar Science III,* Carolyn Watkins, ed., Lunar Science Institute, Contribution No. 88, 1972, pp. 151-155.

[15] Ehmann, W. D., Gillum, D. E., and Morgan, J. W., *Proceedings,* Third Lunar Science Conference, *Geochimica et Cosmochimica Acta,* Supplement 3, Vol. 2, The MIT Press, Cambridge, Mass., 1972, pp. 1149-1160.

[16] Mason, B. and Nelson, W. G., *The Lunar Rocks,* Wiley, New York, 1970, p. 117.

R. Michel,[1] *U. Herpers,*[1] *H. Kulus,*[1] *and W. Herr*[1]

Isotopic Abundance Determination of Submicro Amounts of Rhenium by Neutron Activation

REFERENCE: Michel, R., Herpers, U., Kulus, H., and Herr, W., "Isotopic Abundance Determination of Submicro Amounts of Rhenium by Neutron Activation," *Analytical Methods Developed for Application to Lunar Samples Analyses, ASTM STP 539,* American Society for Testing and Materials, 1973, pp. 140–150.

ABSTRACT: Neutron activation is applied to the isotopic abundance measurements of rhenium in lunar matter. This is achieved by comparing the (n, γ) induced activities of ^{186}Re and ^{188}Re by the 137 keV and the 155 keV γ-line, respectively. Radiochemical processing to a very high purity is needed in order to avoid interferences of ^{199}Au and ^{99m}Tc. Additionally, the rhenium and tungsten contents were determined.

An isotopic anomaly of rhenium was established in Apollo 14 samples, exhibiting a remarkable enrichment of ^{187}Re (1.4 to 1.8 percent in soils and up to 29 percent in the breccia 14321). It is shown that this enrichment is at least partially due to neutron irradiation on the lunar surface by the reaction $^{186}W(n, \gamma)$ $^{187}W \xrightarrow{\beta}$ ^{187}Re. However, the observed anomaly is not produced by lunar neutrons alone. There is also a contribution from the reaction $^{186}W(n, \gamma)$ $^{187}W \xrightarrow{\beta}$ ^{187}Re (n, γ) ^{188}Re in the reactor itself which can be corrected for by the analysis of simultaneously irradiated tungsten standards. The lunar "share" of the ^{187}Re enrichment is found to be 20 to 60 percent of the observed total excess. It is shown that the ^{186}W neutron capture is mainly due to epithermal neutrons (resonances are at 18.8, 171, and 221 eV). Relationships to the recently discovered other neutron induced isotope anomalies in extraterrestrial matter are discussed, and the possibility of deriving neutron spectra and time integrated neutron fluxes is pointed up.

KEY WORDS: lunar analysis, isotopes, neutron activation analysis, rhenium, tungsten, neutron irradiation, neutron flux, neutron spectra, lunar geology, isotopic anomaly

Attempts to measure the isotopic composition of rhenium in lunar material were reported earlier[1].[2] Because of the very small concentrations of rhenium

---

[1] Institut fur Kernchemie der Universitat Koln, Koln, Germany.

[2] The italic numbers in brackets refer to the list of references appended in this paper.

in these samples (down to 0.01 ppb in Apollo 12 igneous rocks[1,2]), the isotopic analysis of rhenium by mass spectrometry is supposed to have no real chance until now. Therefore, the high sensitivity of the activation analysis, especially in combination with radiochemical separations, seemed to be a more realistic approach. Both naturally occurring isotopes ^{185}Re and ^{187}Re have sufficiently large (n, γ) cross sections, σ_{therm} = 105 barn (b) for ^{185}Re and σ_{therm} = 73 b for ^{187}Re[3]. Thus, isotopic ratios can be measured by comparison of the respective induced radioactivities. Counting is done by γ-spectroscopy. Although the 155 kev γ-radiation of ^{188}Re $(T \approx 17$ h) is rather small (absolute intensity is $\sim$ 10 percent only) and the 137 keV γ-line of ^{186}Re $(T \approx 90$ h) $(\sim 9$ percent) is also weak, γ-spectroscopy will have considerable advantages over the more sensitive β-counting technique. The comparison of the two γ-lines of nearly equal intensities allows the detection of both rhenium radioisotopes simultaneously with rather high precision. A slight, but not yet significant enrichment of ^{187}Re was formerly observed[1]. The effect was supposed to be due to lunar neutron capture in ^{186}W[4]. By more improved analytical techniques it was recently possible to prove the existence of a positive abundance anomaly in ^{187}Re for Apollo 14 material, which is due to the ^{186}W(n, γ) ^{187}W $\xrightarrow{\beta^-}$ ^{187}Re process occurring on the lunar surface[5].

Experimental

Lunar samples between 49 to 104 mg were powdered and sealed in high purity quartz. Sample storage and preirradiation handling was done under inertgas (N_2). The ampoules were irradiated together with rhenium and tungsten standards in the FRJ-2 (DIDO-type) reactor at Juelich, ϕ_{therm} = 8 X 10^{13} neutrons (n) cm^{-2} s^{-1} for 12 to 70 h. After transportation and cooling of $\sim$ 6 h the minerals were fused in (covered) nickel crucibles for half an hour with 5 g of sodium hydroxide (NaOH), 0.6 g of sodium peroxide (Na_2O_2), 15 to 20 mg of rhenium (as K ReO$_4$), and 500 mg of tungsten (as WO$_3$) carriers.

Holdback carriers of scandium, lanthanum, cobalt, chromium, antimony, molybdenum, and gold (1 mg each) were prepared in a sodium carbonate matrix.

The melt was dissolved in 100-ml water (H_2O). The solution was heated, ammonium chloride (NH_4Cl) added, and ammonia (NH_3) evaporated. The solution was centrifuged, and the residue was washed with 20 ml of water and the supernatant concentrated to a volume of 40 ml. After the addition of the same volume of concentrate ammonium hydroxide (NH_4OH) rhenium was precipitated by tetraphenylarsonium-chloride $(Ph_4AsCl, 1$ percent) at 50°C. (Tungsten and molybdenum will not interfere under these conditions.) The precipitate was filtered, washed with 10 ml 0.2 percent Ph$_4$AsCl solution and 10 ml water (H_2O) (0°C), and dried at 110°C. Hydrogen (H_2) reduction in a quartz tube at 400 to 600°C was followed by an oxidation with oxygen (O_2). The rhenium heptoxide (Re_2O_7) vapor was collected in a trap $(\sim 100°C)$ and dissolved in 5 ml H_2O (a few drops of NH_4OH and hydrogen peroxide (H_2O_2) added). After boiling for 5 min the (5 to 6 ml) solution was adjusted to 2 N hydrochloric acid (HCl) and passed through a strong-base anion exchanger (Dowex 1 × 8, 200 to 400 mesh, Cl⁻ form; column ϕ = 0.5 cm, 10 cm in length). ReO_4 was eluated under pressure (1.3 atm) with a 0.15 N HCl, containing 5 percent of ammoniumthiocyanate at a rate of 1 ml/min. The first 5.5 to 7 ml of the eluate are free from SCN⁻ and were discarded. The following main fraction of about 20 ml contains over 90 percent of the rhenium freed from Tc-99m. Because SCN⁻ and NO_3^- ions interfere in the precipitation of Ph_4AsReO_4, they had to be destroyed. (SCN⁻ by nitric acid (HNO_3) the latter by evaporating with concentrated HCl. After dilution to 50 ml the free acid concentration sulfuric acid H_2SO_4) from SCN⁻ and HCl) is lowered by addition of NaOH and the rhenium (VII) is precipitated with Ph_4AsCl (10 ml; 1 percent solution). The precipitate was washed, dried, and weighed. The chemical yield was ∼ 70 percent.

The dry distillation and the ion exchange procedure are necessary to remove traces of ^{99m}Tc and [199]Au. As can be seen from Fig. 1 they seriously counteract with their 143 and 158 keV γ-lines.

Counting was done by a heavily shielded 25 cm³ Ge (Li) detector combined with a 4096 channel analyzer. Since in this case an absolute proof of the radiochemical purity is not possible by means of γ-spectroscopy only, we found it necessary to also check the half-lives. Because the half-lives of [188]Re and of [186]Re were encumbered with considerable uncertainties (literature values

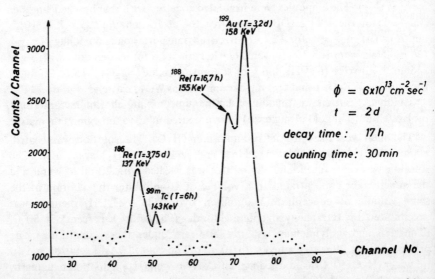

FIG. 1–[99m]Tc and [199]Au interference in the [186]Re, [188]Re spectrum of the chondrite "Ramsdorf."

ranged from 16.0 to 18.9 h for ^{188}Re and from 88.9 to 92.8 h for ^{186}Re) a redetermination was performed. This work resulted in: $T_{1/2} = 90.64 \pm 0.09$ h for ^{186}Re and $T_{1/2} = 16.98 \times 0.02$ h for ^{188}Re[6]. The errors are lower by a factor of 2 and 10, respectively, than those of earlier determinations. The ^{186}Re and ^{188}Re decay was followed for at least 5 to 6 half-lives. The individual samples were counted 10 times each. γ-spectra were stored on papertape and processed by a PDP9 computer. Background subtraction and correction for decay were followed by a least square fit. The elemental abundance of rhenium in lunar samples are based on ^{186}Re, assuming a terrestrial isotopic abundance of (stable) ^{185}Re = 37.07 percent[7]. The errors correspond to one standard deviation.

The tungsten was separated from the ($\sim$ 100 ml) filtrate of the first rhenium precipitation. After having eliminated the excess of NH_3 by heat 10 mg ammonium orthophosphate (($NH_4)_2$ HPO_4) holdback carrier was added. (^{32}P may raise the background by way of its Bremsstrahlung.) After the addition of 20 ml of concentrated H_2SO_4 and a short heating period, the yellow tungstic acid ($H_2 WO_4$) was precipitated and washed. The tungstic acid was dissolved in an excess of ammonia, diluted to 50 ml, heated, and reprecipitated with 40 ml of concentrated HNO_3. This step was repeated. The sample was then dried and heated to 700°C. The WO_3 yield reached 75 to 80 percent. The tungsten content was determined independently by the ^{187}W three main γ-lines of 134, 479, and 686 keV, respectively.

In Fig. 2 a typical rhenium γ-spectrum of the breccia 14321 is compared with that of a terrestrial rhenium standard.

Obviously, the ^{188}Re peak (155 keV) of the breccia is several times higher than the "terrestrial" ^{188}Re peak, indicating an excess of ^{187}Re. The effect becomes even more pronounced with regard to the actual counting and decay times. An attempt to explain this enrichment by the lunar process ^{186}W(n, γ) ^{187}W $\underset{\rightarrow}{\beta}$ ^{187}Re meets the difficulty that in our analytical procedure a second neutron bombardment took place. Evidently, the process ^{186}W(n, γ) ^{187}W $\underset{\rightarrow}{\beta}$ ^{187}Re $(n, \gamma)^{188}$Re occurs during the terrestrial neutron irradiation and can simulate a ^{187}Re enhancement. Therefore, it was necessary to prove to what extent the observed isotopic effect is due to lunar neutron irradiation or due to reactor activation. In order to do this, an aliquot of our WO_3 standard was first analyzed for its rhenium content and then the rhenium isotopic composition was also checked.

Since we were obliged to use different reactor positions, we had to determine, in all cases, the pile production of ^{188}Re from tungsten. ^{186}W has previously been used as a monitor for intermediate neutrons[8]. However, because the resonance integrals of ^{186}W for the respective irradiation positions are not known with the precision needed, we were not able to make the necessary correction for ^{188}Re breeding on the basis of calculation only.

In Fig. 3 spectra of a pure tungsten standard and of a mixed tungsten plus

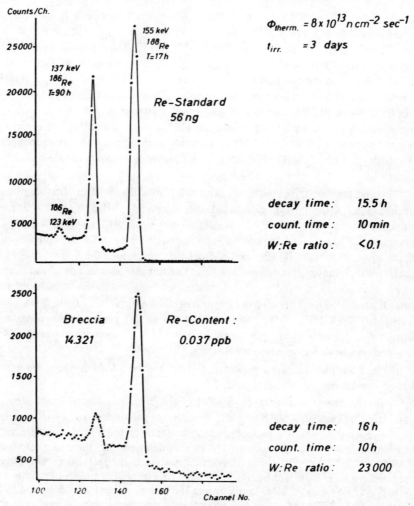

FIG. 2—*Comparison of neutron activated terrestrial and lunar rhenium γ-ray spectra.*

rhenium standard are presented. The shape of the spectra merely represents the relative positive abundance effect of [187]Re. So it is possible to simulate the shape of the "lunar" rhenium spectrum of the breccia 14321 by preparing a mixed standard with an identical tungsten/rhenium ratio. These spectra indicate strikingly the necessity to differentiate between the [187]Re produced in the reactor and that produced on the lunar surface. On the other hand, it shows that it is possible to determine very precisely the contribution of the "terrestrial"

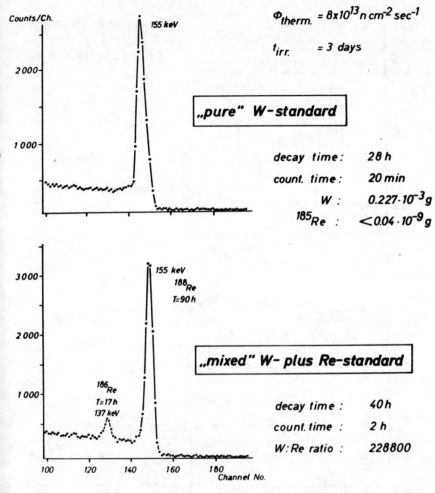

FIG. 3—*γ-ray spectra of rhenium from irradiated tungsten and tungsten plus rhenium standards demonstrating the production of* ^{188}Re *by the reaction* $^{186}W(n, \gamma)$ ^{187}W $\xrightarrow{\beta}$ ^{187}Re (n, γ) ^{188}Re.

^{188}Re production. In order to decrease the absolute amount of reactor made ^{187}Re, the pile irradiation has to be minimized.

It should be mentioned that the formation of ^{186}Re from ^{184}W is negligible, since the cross section for ^{184}W is comparably small ($\sigma_{therm} = 1.9$ b) and the 70 day half-life of ^{185}W leads to a rather slow growth of ^{186}Re.

The significance of the lunar excess of ^{187}Re and simultaneously the amount

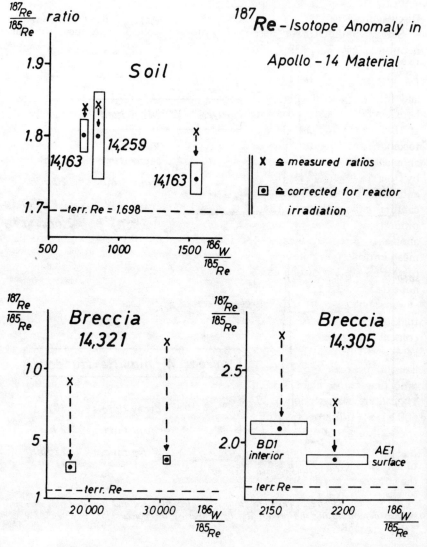

FIG. 4—*Results of the rhenuim isotopic analysis of Apollo 14 material.*

of terrestrial enhancement in ^{187}Re is seen in Fig. 4 where the ^{187}Re/^{185}Re ratios are plotted against the ^{186}W/^{185}Re ratios. The measured as well as the corrected values are presented. The errors are those of the total analysis. As can be seen from these diagrams the enhancement in ^{187}Re due to lunar neutrons is in all cases significant.

Discussion

Several authors have described isotopic anomalies produced by lunar neutrons. Thermal neutron capture has been found in ^{157}Gd and in ^{155}Gd[9,10], and in ^{150}Sm, ^{152}Sm[11]. Epithermal capture was discovered for ^{79}Br and ^{81}Br resulting in anomalous abundances of ^{80}Kr and ^{81}Kr[10], and for ^{130}Ba producing ^{131}Xe[12,13]. The ^{186}W/^{187}Re anomaly described here surely will be due to epithermal neutron capture in ^{186}W having resonances at 18.8, 171, and 221 eV[14]. It is interesting to note that all the anomalies due to epithermal capture are observed in the form of "positive" abundance anomalies of the product nuclides, quite in contrast to those which are produced by thermal neutron capture which were measured as "negative" abundance anomalies of the target nuclides. The latter are favored by extremely high capture cross sections. The relative magnitude of the negative effects is proportional to the (n, γ) cross section averaged over the fluence. Positive anomalies—in contrast—are proportional to the product of this time integrated mean cross section times the ratio (target-element/product-element). ^{186}W has a (n,γ) cross section of only 35 b at 0.0253 eV, and its excitation function does not exceed 40 b[14].

Assuming this, the tungsten/rhenium anomaly could be measured only if the tungsten-rhenium ratio is extremely high. In Table 1 the rhenium and tungsten contents of our samples analyzed are compared, and the tungsten/rhenium ratios are given. This ratio is > 1000 in all cases, and it is even higher in breccias and igneous rocks. In 14321 it reaches the extremely high value of 41.000 (cosmic ratio tungsten/rhenium = 3.63[15]). Combining those values with the effective $1/v$ capture cross section of ^{186}W which for Apollo 11 material has a value of $\sim$ 600 b[16], it follows that the ^{187}Re isotope effect is the second largest positive abundance anomaly in lunar material next to the ^{130}Ba/^{131}Xe anomaly.

For the interpretation the respective cross sections averaged over the flux are of special interest. From experiments the numbers of neutrons (ϵ_w) is equal to the cross section averaged over the time integrated flux.

If Δ^{187}Re(lun) is the number of ^{187}Re atoms produced on the lunar surface ϵ_w can be given in good approximation by the quotient Δ^{187}Re(lun)/^{186}W. In Table 2 quantitative data are presented from which this quotient is derived. The absolute amounts of ^{186}W and the excess of ^{187}Re in columns 2 to 4 are normalized to a 50 mg sample weight. From column 2 follows that the total excess in ^{187}Re ranges from ($\sim$2 to $\sim$12) $\times$ 10^{-12} g. The lunar fraction (column 5) is between 20 to 60 percent of this amount. In the last column the ratio Δ^{187}Re(lun)/^{186}W results in a relatively wide spread from 0.027 to 0.18 $\times$ 10^{-3}. These data may be of considerable value for theoretical calculations on the interaction of cosmic rays with the lunar surface, especially with regard to the neutron production rate and neutron energy spectrum.

Lunar neutron spectra have been calculated by Armstrong and Alsmiller[17]

TABLE 1–*Rhenium and tungsten contents of lunar material.*

Sample		Type	W, ppm	Re,[a] ppb	Ratio W:Re, $\times 10^3$
14.163	a	soil	1.32 ± 0.02	1.316 ± 0.004	1.1
	b	(< 1 mm)	1.94 ± 0.03	0.957 ± 0.007	2.0
0.259	a	soil	1.56 ± 0.02	1.41 ± 0.03	1.1
	b	(< 1 mm)	1.85 ± 0.03	1.16 ± 0.04	1.6
0.321	a	breccia	0.82 ± 0.01		
	b		0.86 ± 0.01	0.021 ± 0.002	40.9
	c		0.87 ± 0.01	0.037 ± 0.004	23.3
0.305 BD1 integrated		breccia	1.74 ± 0.03	0.620 ± 0.003	2.8
0.305 AE1 surface			2.39 ± 0.03	0.834 ± 0.003	2.9
12.053		rock	0.12[b]	0.033 ± 0.002 ⎫ 0.030 ± 0.003 ⎬ 0.026 ± 0.002 ⎭	4.0
0.021		rock	0.28 ± 0.01	0.077 ± 0.007 0.078 ± 0.007	3.6

[a] Rhenium contents based on $^{185}Re(n,\gamma)$ $^{186}Re(T = 90.6$ h).
[b] Given by Wänke et al (1971).

TABLE 2–*Contribution of the reactor irradiation to the ^{187}Re anomaly.*

Apollo 14 Samples	$\Delta^{187}Re$ Brutto, 10^{-12} g	$\Delta^{187}Re$ Reactor, 10^{-12} g	$\Delta^{187}Re$ Lunar, 10^{-12} g	^{186}W, 10^{-9} g	$\dfrac{\Delta^{187}Re \text{ (lun)}}{^{186}W}$, $\times 10^{-3}$
14.163	3.5	0.94	2.6 ± 0.3	18.8	0.14 ± 0.01
	1.9	1.21	0.7 ± 0.3	27.6	0.027 ± 0.01
0.259	3.8	1.13	2.6 ± 1.4	22.2	0.12 ± 0.06
0.321	3.9	3.18	0.7 ± 0.09	10.7	0.071 ± 0.007
	5.1	4.13	1.0 ± 0.09	12.4	0.081 ± 0.006
0.305 BD1 integrated	11.9	7.39	4.5 ± 0.3	24.8	0.18 ± 0.01
0.305 AE1 surface	8.9	6.21	2.7 ± 0.2	33.9	0.081 ± 0.005

NOTE–All data normalized to 50 mg weight (individual weights 49 to 104 mg).

and by Lingenfelter et al[16,18]. For the moment, only the later will be suitable here, because these calculations take into account the capture rates of those nuclides which show n-produced isotope effects. Though Lingenfelter et al estimate an error of ~ 80 percent for the absolute normalization of the time integrated flux, it should be possible to check the shape of their neutron spectra. In principle this could be done by comparing the experimental capture rates of different capturing isotopes with those derived theoretically. However, certain difficulties exist in so far as the effective macroscopic cross sections of the lunar material are only given with the uncertainties of the chemical analysis. Nevertheless, within these uncertainties the isotopic anomalies measured show that the calculations are in the right order. Evidently, more experimental data as well as more detailed calculations are needed. The rather small $\epsilon_w = 0.027 \times 10^{-3}$ for the soil 14163 points up a relatively low neutron exposure for this particular sample. A possible explanation would be that tungsten is often concentrated in individual metallic grains. (Tungsten contents up to 223 ppm are reported by Wlotzka et al[19].) Possibly, the presence of such metallic fragments which might have received very few neutrons only, would reduce the apparent neutron dose of the total (50 mg) soil sample.

Obviously, isotopic abundance measurements on lunar rhenium by means of neutron activation can be regarded as a very useful tool for cosmochemical studies, including such delicate problems as the energy spectra of lunar neutrons and the radiation history of the moon.

References

[1] Herr, W., Herpers, U., Michel, R., Rassoul, A. A. Abdel, and Woelfle, R., *Proceedings, Second Lunar Science Conference, Geochimica et Cosmochimica Acta,* Supplement 2, Vol. 2, The MIT Press, Cambridge, Mass., 1971, pp. 1337-1341.

[2] Lovering, J. F. and Butterfield, D., *Proceedings,* Apollo 11 Lunar Science Conference, *Geochimica et Cosmochimica Acta,* Supplement 1, Pergamon, New York, Vol. 2, 1970, pp. 1351-1355.

[3] Seelmann-Eggebert, W., Pfennig, G., and Münzel, H., *Chart of the Nuclides, Der Bundesminister für Wissenschaftliche Forschung,* Bonn, ed., issued by Gersbach and Sohn Verlag, München.

[4] Herpers, U., Michel, R., and Herr, W., *Angewandte Chemie,* Vol. 10, 1971, pp. 818-867. (International edition in English).

[5] Michel, R., Herpers, U., Kulus, H., and Herr, W., *Proceedings,* Third Lunar Science Conference, *Geochimica et Cosmochimica Acta,* Supplement 3, Vol. 2, 1972, The MIT Press, Cambridge, Mass., pp. 1917-1925.

[6] Michel, R. and Herpers, U., *Radiochimica Acta,* Vol. 16, 1971, pp. 115-116.

[7] White, J. R. and Cameron, A. E., *Physical Review,* Vol. 74, 1948, pp. 991-1000.

[8] Zijp, W. L. in *Neutron Fluence Measurements,* International Atomic Energy Agency, Vienna, 1970, pp. 77-140.

[9] Albee, A. L., Burnett, D. S., Chodos, A. A., Eugster, O. J., Hunecke, J. C., Papanastassiou, D. A., Podosek, F. A., Russ, G. P., III, Sanz, H. G., Tera, F., and Wasserburg, G. J., *Science,* Vol. 167, 1970, pp. 463-366.

[10] Lugmair, G. W. and Marti, K., *Earth and Planet Science Letters,* Vol. 13, 1972, pp. 32-42.

[11] Russ, G. P., III, Burnett, D. S., Lingenfelter, R. E., and Wasserburg, G. J., *Earth and Planet Science Letters,* Vol. 13, 1972, pp. 53-60.

[12] Kaiser, W. A. and Berman, B. L., "The Integral $^{130}Ba(n, \gamma)$ Cross Section and the Origin of ^{131}Xe on the Moon," to be submitted to the *Earth and Planet Science Letters,* 1971.

[13] Eberhardt, P., Geiss, J., Graf, H., Groegler, N., Kraehenbuehl, U., Schwaller, H., Schwarzmueller, J., and Stettler, A., *Earth and Planet Science Letters,* Vol. 10, 1970, pp. 67-72.

[14] Goldberg, M. D., Nughabghal, S. F., Purohit, S. N., Maurno, B. A., and May, V. M., *Neutron Cross Sections,* Vol. 11 C, BNL-325, 1966.

[15] Seuss, H. and Urey, H. C., *Reviews of Modern Physics,* Vol. 28, 1956, pp. 53-74.

[16] Lingenfelter, R. E., Canfield, E. H., and Hampel, V. H., "The Lunar Neutron Flux Revisited," to be submitted to the *Earth and Planet Science Letters,* 1972.

[17] Armstrong, T. W. and Alsmiller, R. G., *Proceedings,* Second Lunar Science Conference, *Geochimica et Cosmochimica Acta,* Supplement 2, Vol. 2, The MIT Press, Cambridge, Mass., pp. 1729-1745.

[18] Lingenfelter, R. E., Canfield, E. H., and Hess, W. N., *Journal of Geophysical Research,* Vol. 66, 1961, pp. 2665-2671.

[19] Wlotzka, F., Jagoutz, E., Spettel, B., Baddenhausen, H., Balacescu, A., and Waenke, H. in *Lunar Science III,* Carolyn Watkins, ed., Lunar Science Institute, Contract No. 88, 1972, pp. 806-808.